CLERICAL MISTAKE

CLERICAL MISTAKE

Anthony Williams

Clerical Mistake

Copyright © 2015 by Anthony Williams

ALL RIGHTS RESERVED

No portion of this publication may be reproduced, stored in any electronic system, or transmitted in any form or by any means, electronic, mechanical, photocopy, recording or otherwise, without written permission from the author. Brief quotations may be used in literary reviews.

Cover art by: Frozen Films

Library of Congress Control Number:
IBSN: 978-0-692-59315-8

www.pppplus4inmates.org

This book is a work of fiction. All characters and events are a product of the author's creative literary style. All characters and names are used fictitiously. Any resemblance to any actual person, or persons, events, places, or portrayal whether living, or dead is purely coincidental.

Acknowledgements

Dan Holly, author of "Sometimes You Get the Bear." He is the main reason for my attempt to become a writer. With sincere thanks to Jane Pincus, for her superb guidance and clique editorial assistance. Without her none of this would have happened. Her timing was God sent. Cassie Sutton, a very old friend who pushed me in the beginning when all this was a blur. My other friend Willis Mills, whose kind help made the biggest difference in the way this story came together. Joseph Auche and Robert Alvarez, for coming through at a time when they were needed most. My brother Bryan Harris and good friend James Sanders for their criticism. Dustin White and Duron Lee made what might have seemed impossible reachable. Lastly the most important persons are mother Mrs. Ginger Harris and, sister Brenda and Vaughn McMillian. They worked and supported me in all areas to get this book completed.

PREFACE

This story is about a 42 year old man incarcerated for the first time. It is based on a true story. Juwan chronicled his journey through a gauntlet of achievements and failures. It is a compelling tale of lust, greed, selfishness, betrayal, loss, reunion, reconciliation and love. Juwan's account of what he experienced being thrust into the legal system by corrupt public servants on all levels. He learned the true meaning of the term "clerical mistake" before he could understand, and expose the unethical behavior of officers of the courts which had taken an oath to protect and serve the public, but for their own personal gain. Unfortunately, they have betrayed everything they swore to. This story will compel you to view everything and everyone from a different perspective. Juwan discovered a hidden talent in understanding the judicial system and developed a newfound appreciation for life, true friendship and family. He became an advocate for justice within the correctional system in the United States.

TABLE OF CONTENTS

Introduction

On a nice July night, I was smiling to myself, cruising down I-95 South, doing 85 mph in my Sabina designed Aston Martin AM 10 to handle some business. There were no state troopers in sight and very little traffic. I had popped a CD in to listen to some old school vibes, with Marvin Gaye's sexual healing in the background. I was at the top of my game. With everything a man could want. My health, beautiful women all around me, a stack treetop tall. I was in my prime. Not a care in the world. It felt good to know that whatever I commanded would come to me. Everyone who was anyone, wanted to be in my company to do business with me. I had arrived, the American dream come true. I felt like another John Gotti, sweet! Then suddenly I heard a deep voice yelling, "Get up!" And once again I awoke to find myself in my 8x10 cage as a 6'5", 300 pound guard stared down at me! Oh God, why did I have to wake up?

Part 1

It Started Off Like A Dream That Could Have Tilted Either Way. Then A Tremendous Event Took Place That Caused Juwan Jackson's Downfall.

Chapter 1

Richer Than Ever But You Can't Buy Tomorrow YMCA

The alarm went off. I reached over darn near knocking it off the end table at 5:57 a.m. I had to make a lot of moves before 9 a.m., but I didn't want to tear myself away from my double king size bed and these black satin sheets. I thought to myself it's Monday morning. I needed to get up and go stack my benjamins for an upcoming party I was giving Terence the weekend of May 26, 2002. Terence is my little brother from another mother, but I love him all the same. He liked being called Big Fish and considered himself a great white shark, the smoothest promoter who ever placed his feet on the "Dirty South" soil. As I sat on the edge of the bed, my mind kept racing through all the past events we'd created and all the calls I had to make so all the right people could get the 411 that it's on for Memorial Day in Miami. As I stepped into my shower of Italian marble with 6 gold plated waterspouts, I thought of the itinerary for the coming weekend. Busta Rhymes birthday party on Friday, a Ja-Rule party on Saturday, a Ludacris party on Sunday. That sounded about right. I turned the shower on full blast and wished I could have slept a little longer. But business is business. I had to get on my grind. I turned the water on as hot as possible.

It poured all over my body messaging my skin, steam filling the room. I thought about the meeting I'd had with Muhsin, the NFL football player when he had stopped by my office to discuss how his company, a nonprofit and my company, Frozen Films, could work together on a lucrative project. I'd invited him into my conference room to work out the details. Muhsin wanted to commit me and my company to a contract to film his company's documentary for the sports channel. In the deal, he offered me profit-sharing on the individual sales of the merchandise we'd be selling.

It sounded like "money in the bank". We made the deal. I'd also been in on a conference call with executives of a major production company, Danger Inc. The CEO had asked me to collaborate with them on various ventures. Naturally, I was for almost anything that was going to promise an increase for me. I felt absolutely successful, euphoric. No righteous man could have asked for more and not feel even greedier. Suddenly my cell phone rang. It was Jack, a guy who claims to be the best mechanic and car salesman in the south. I took his word for it. I did not discover until later that he was as sleazy and greasy as they come. I've seen a lot of characters in my day, but Jack was a new breed of slim shady, who loved tooting his own horn. He attempted to manipulate everyone who came in contact with him with smoke and mirrors more so than anything. He eventually became my worst nightmare. If only I had paid attention to what was right in front of me. Everything in my being screamed for me to cut Jack loose. Something wasn't right. "Jack … what's up?" He needed to see me about some business as soon as possible. I agreed to meet him outside the YMCA in an hour. He said cool and hung up. It was coming up on 6 p.m.. I dressed in my blood-red Pirelli sweatsuit and my black Gucci loafers and headed to the elevator to hit the gym just across the street. I thought to myself, after my workout I'll worry about hooking up with Jack and see what he had up his sleeve this time to try and separate me from my profits. My cell rang, it was Jack again. Okay! I hurried to clean off the sweat I had built up and got dressed. As I was headed for the door Ronda called asking where I was. I explained I was working out at the Y. Before I could say more, she said she'd be right there. Stepping outside, I saw 2 white dudes and one black guy just standing around. I told Ronda I'd catch her later, I had to go and walked a few yards to give myself some space. I looked around expecting Jack, but he was nowhere to be found. I reached in my jacket and pulled out my cell to call him up. What was taking him so long? Before I could complete the call, one of the white dudes, rolled up. Before I could think, I was face-to-face with a 9mm. One of the guys shouted, "Hey you on the ground now!" I thought that shout wasn't meant for me. When I heard "you in the red sweatsuit", my life flashed before my eyes. This had to be a joke. I could not believe I was being mugged in broad daylight. Then I heard someone shouting. "Police!" The next thing I knew, I was slammed onto the ground, the wind knocked out of me. I could not begin to figure out why the police had crushed my face against the concrete with their knees on my neck. That was the first violation. It felt like four football players on my back. I knew they were trying to save themselves the paperwork of taking me down to the station and writing their reports. They were strangling me. I was being crushed where I lay by South Carolina's finest. In all the commotion, I couldn't help but wonder out of the 4 people who had been standing in front of the "Y", the police had chosen to grab me. It was like being in the Twilight Zone. I could not wake up. I soon discovered why I was flying solo in this nightmare. They were all undercover. It was a sting operation! Before I knew it I was handcuffed, surrounded by what seemed like 25 cops all glaring down at me. I shouted, "What the heck is going on? These handcuffs are too tight! I can't feel my fingers." The next thing I knew they pulled me up by my shoulders to my feet. I was angry. "Why am I being arrested? What's your name? Give me your badge number!" I had always prided myself for being a top-notch businessman and a lover of women, but the way these officers were handling me I felt like a hooker with a pimp pressuring me about his money. This was more than I could stand. A crowd gathering. This was definitely an "I don't need to be here moment." It was humiliating!

The Judge

September 8, 2003, I found myself handcuffed standing in the courtroom staring at a Judge named Ms. Eve. She entered and took her seat. The bailiff ordered everyone to be seated. He stated the case The State of South Carolina v. Juwan Jackson. Case numbers CRS02401 and CRS02402. The judge asked if The State was ready to proceed. Mr. Blue, the Assistant District Attorney, waived his opening statements.

My Attorney, Mr. Ericson, proceeded with his opening statements mentioning to the jury that they were going to hear unfounded accusations about his client being a pornographic filmmaker, with an estimated earning of 6-figures a year. While my attorney was presenting his opening statements, my mind started to drift. I needed to be somewhere else. I couldn't believe I was sitting in this courtroom on trial simply for standing in front of the YMCA. When they locked me up my stuff was tight. Everything I was doing was legit. I was crossing my T's and dotting my I's. What did I miss? Then I thought about my girl, Jamille. Jamille was about to move to Atlanta to start her new life without me. We had been together since 1995. Jamille was my "whatever clever" chick. She had held me down straight out the gate but she wasn't here anymore. My heart dropped. Things were not cool between us. We had begun to grow apart. After 7 years, she decided she wanted to find her own way. I still love her, but it was time to let her move on. That was what she really wanted. Besides, I had a new woman who promised to make all my other girlfriends absolutely unnecessary. Right about now I needed to believe she would deliver. Her name was Sharon. Sharon, at 50 years my vintage piece. Married with 2 teenage sons, she had a failing marriage and a very ill father who she had to take care of. She was very successful, the owner and operator of 14 McDonald's restaurants, all located in Columbia, South Carolina. She was great in bed. Her old and new tricks are broken down to a science. Who could resist my new sugar momma?

The Set Up

It's 7:30 a.m. and I'm almost done cleaning up the kitchen after making some breakfast when my cell phone rang. I answered it on the 3rd ring. "Hello! Frozen Films, how can I help you?"

A man whispered, "Hey it's me, Jack. I'm just calling to let you know that I'm going to a car auction today. Do you still want to come with me?"

I answered, "Sure, what time?"

Jack said he's going to have to get back to me on that cause he'd stayed out all night and was in trouble with his wife. He said, "When I call you back later, I'm going to be talking like I'm buying 2 car rims for my wife because that's the only way she'll let me leave! So play along when I call?"

My response was, "Whatever works."

The Count Down

As soon as I hung up, my secretary Cassandra called to ask me what I was doing and did I need for her to come in a little bit early today?

"I'm in my office on the computer looking for footage to use for my Canadian contract with Platinum Disk. It's a big contract!

"Yeah, I know. That's why I called. Okay, I'll be there in 10 minutes. Do you need me to pick up anything?"

"No! I ate already."

Cassandra's 22 years old, brown-skinned country girl with a New Yorker attitude. I could call her any time of the day or night. I admire that about her. All my business associates wanted to steal her from me but, Cassandra stayed loyal to me.

By 8:15 p.m., I sent the elevator down to her. I had left my front door open so she could walk right in. She was wearing a tight fitted leather skirt and vest outfit, with a lot of skin showing. She couldn't help herself. She knew she was fit and she wanted everyone to know it too.

Only a very few people were allowed to meet me in my office. When Cassandra walked in I had been editing some footage of shows I'd done with The Carolina Show Stoppers and other motorcycle stunt teams. I decided to run it on my plasma flat screen.

She sat down next to me. Although she was only 22 years old, she had complete muscle control over her entire body. I admired a woman who knew to stay on top of her game, by staying physically fit.

At times we would work out for at least 45 minutes, a lot of time to give up from my hectic schedule.

Cassandra would cook, clean my apartment, and drive me anywhere I needed to go. She was irreplaceable.

Win-Win Situation

I fell soundly asleep. At 11:30 p.m., I was awakened by another call from Marilyn, my girl before Jamille. "Hello, Frozen Films. How can I help you?"

"You can help me by coming home!" Marilyn refused to let go. We had hooked up a few months before I met Jamille in 1995. I needed to have a little of what both Jamille and Marilyn had to offer me so I kept them both around. When things started to get a little too wild, I made a choice and decided to leave Marilyn for Jamille in 1999. When I told Marilyn I was busy and would call her back later, she hung up! She managed the Embassy Suites Hotel in Columbia, S.C. and we'd met at her hairdressers' beauty salon when I stopped by to see the salons owner Keith. I was looking into becoming his partner. He was finishing up Marilyn's hair. She was very attractive.

I said, "Okay, I think I can give her a ride home."

We all smiled. Keith, a homosexual with a spectacular clientele, styles professional basketball players and their wives' hair. Even the female judges in town had their hair done there. He was as flamboyant as they come and only served local and visiting celebrities. By word of mouth, all the women wanted an appointment at Keith's beauty salon. I did drive Marilyn home, we exchanged numbers. After about 2 to 3 weeks, she gave me the keys to her house. She made sure to cook for me whether I came over or not, always hoping. By the time I was arrested in 2002, she had moved on and gotten married but she would call me from time to time asking me to come home. I would laugh and ask her how married life was treating her. She was happy because her husband had a '9 to 5' and came straight home every night to eat her famous chicken and dumplings. Jamille and I had stopped eating meat in 1998. I had almost forgotten how good Marilyn's cooking really was. I didn't start eating meat again until 2002.

Lock Down

Jamille came to visit me in the county jail all the way from Atlanta. I was happy to see her. She noticed I was not the man she had left. She said I looked undernourished and recommended that I start eating meat while I'm on lockdown. I stood up to show her I still had my 6 pack. I still was as solid as granite. I was on lockdown in the county jail for 8 days after my arrest until I could make bond for $100,000. I had come in weighing 220 lbs, but my weight quickly fell off because I could not eat the food there. I could not recognize exactly what it was they were serving me. It looked foreign to me. At the time I suffered from a delicate palate. Because of my affliction, I lost about 30 lbs. in 8 days.

After making bond, my friend Karen came to pick me up but before I got out, Karen and my mom went to my apartment to gather what was left after the police ransacked my place and confiscated anything and everything they considered to be evidence against me, leaving only food and clothes.

When I was released Karen picked me up. From there we drove to her house, a $250,000 house near a big lake. It was peaceful out there. I really enjoyed it. I especially liked the fact it was far away from the city limits.

I wondered how Karen could afford a place like this but thought better not to ask.

I had only slept with her a few times, but hanging around her I became a super freak. It was a mistake to stay with her not only because we were not married, but because everybody in town knew she was crazy. But I didn't care. I had to have her. We had been friends for so long that I thought I'd eventually free myself from her seducing allure. How wrong I was.

We had not had sex in a while. Karen did not make any exceptions. Once you slept with her you belonged to her, until she was finished with you. She'd slay anybody she slept with whenever the relationship was over!

I knew a few men who had been in a long term relationship with her. One had graduated from college receiving a $90,000,000 basketball contract. The first thing he did was proposed marriage to Karen.

Another guy who was dating a celebrity singer and songwriter wanted to keep both relationships going, but he chose Karen.

A reputable physician diagnostic conclusion of Karen's condition concluded that she suffered for schizophrenia and a designer curved uterus. Karen could have any man she wanted. She warned me of how good she felt inside. Her actions confirmed it but I had to learn the hard way. I used to call her up at 3 or 4 o'clock in the morning on my way home from the club hoping she didn't have company. She would tell me all about her dramatics of the day. She would tell me about these men who would be at her beck and call and how she could get them to do anything for her. Some of the things that flew out her mouth were crazy. I'd laugh non-stop. She enjoyed sharing detailed personal information with anyone who'd listen. I lived with her for 6 months. It was like living with Dr. Jekyll and Mr. Hyde. I was addicted and she knew it.

Karen was 6 feet tall with a light brown skinned complexion with long brownish red hair and freckles. Most of the town's females hated her. She was a man-eater.

September 9, 2002

It's 4:15 p.m. My cell phone rang. It's my good friend Carolyn from California. "Hello! Hello, hey baby it's me. I'm in your city." I was always happy to hear from Carolyn. "Where are you? Do you need me to pick you up?"

"No, I'm at the airport picking up my rental right now. What are you doing?"

"I want you to take me and my friend Saundra to that Spanish restaurant again. We love that place."

"Okay, I can do that. How long you think it will take you to get here?"

"I'll have my car in 10 minutes, but I have to swing by and pick up Saundra and we'll be at your house by 5 p.m."

"Okay that'll work, see you then." I hung up. At 4:25 p.m. another call came in. It was Jack. "Hello! Hello, I hear you loud and clear! It's me, Jack."

"Hey Jack, what's up? What time are we going to the car auction?"

Jack responded, "I'm on my way to Columbia. I just need to pick up my daughter, drop her off, tow a car right quick, pick up my money and I'll be on my way to you."

I asked him where he wanted to meet up at. He didn't answer right away. I said, "I'll be at the YMCA working out. Call me when you're done and I'll come outside."

At 5:15 p.m., Carolyn called for me to send the elevator down. She came straight up to my apartment without Saundra. When she stepped off the elevator, I thought how delicious she looked, a real seductress. I wanted to bend her like a pretzel, but I had other engagements that had to be handled first. She was enchanting and I knew I was weak-minded when it came to beautiful women, but business would always be business. It came first!

I showed her my latest footage of the Millennium Bike Show. I explained that I had to cut this visit short because I had to go to a car auction. Her body language showed she was upset but understood.

I knew she came a long way and intended to devour me since she had me on her mental rotisserie. I needed to get away from her as fast as possible before she had her way with me and serve me up on her platter.

I grabbed my house keys and said, "You can finish watching the footage; just make sure everything is tight when you leave. I'll call the restaurant and let them know you're coming so everything will be on the house."

She smiled in a disappointed sinister way as she watched me rush up outta there. I thought to myself, "Finally made it to the Y."

I looked at my watch and it was 5:30 p.m. It felt like time was flying today. I went to my locker and changed into my workout gear. I managed to get in a little workout before Jack called at 6:15 p.m. He said he was pulling up to the YMCA.

I said, "Okay."

He asked if I still have both sets of rims. I said yes and hung up. My phone would not stop ringing. Call after call, I stood there waiting for Jack to drive up. I never paid any attention to how fast the cars rode by before today. I didn't know which car he would be in and it didn't matter. My mind was on getting another vehicle and making it back to Carolyn!

Chapter 2

It's Not Easy Avoiding the Sleazy
The PCT

I eventually found myself down in the precinct being questioned in a small dirty room with my hands still cuffed behind my back. I started to observe my surroundings and noticed a large 2-way mirror, an empty chair facing me, and a beat-up table between me and the chair. I looked up only to see a camera facing down at me. Before I knew it I was surrounded by the same guys who had slammed me to the ground in front of the Y. Alcohol, Tobacco, Firearms (A.T.F.) and Explosive Bureau Agent Carl Black and Columbia, South Carolina, police officer the Rick "Notorious" Buster. It took me a while to discover who they were because when I was asking they weren't telling. Rick took the lead and started the interrogation. While he questioned me I kept asking myself, "What in the heck is happening? Why am I in this filthy room at the police station?"

Rick B and Black were taking turns questioning me about drugs, asking me whose stuff was found in the back of the Escalade. I couldn't help it but when they mentioned drugs I started to sweat. I just know these crooked cops are not trying to pin some bogus drug charge on my behind; no way, no how. I started feeling like Dorothy in the Wizard of Oz. I wanted to do like she did, click my darn heels so I could find myself back in Brooklyn far away from any setup artist.

I had no idea why they were questioning me about drugs that were found in the car of an acquaintance.

I asked, "What stuff are you talking about?" At least 7 officers picked me up at the YMCA. Why not ask them whose drugs they had found. I'd triggered a nerve in Rick B. His face became contorted.

My first instinct was to run for the door, but I quickly came to my senses and just froze. I felt myself shaking. Mind you, I was still handcuffed surrounded by unfriendlies in a locked room with no chance of getting out unless they let me out. I had to fight off the urge to break down and cry.

Buster who seemed to be in charge, slayed me when he started to shout at me and began banging on the table. He claimed I had been under investigation for 6 months and that he knew how old I was, were my mother lived and every move I had been making, that he knew everything about me.

I was floored. My imagination started to work double time. I could not believe that while I was going about my everyday life minding my own business without a care in the world, Rick B was clocking my every move. It all came down to dragging me into a precinct and accusing me of drug possession by a malicious crew of street thugs with badges. I was in disbelief. I thought to myself, "This is nonsense. I have to get out of here. These son of a guns are serious."

I started to feel lightheaded so I thought I'd better ask to make a phone call. I desperately needed to connect to anyone outside this building. I asked to use the telephone and the men's room. Neither Black nor Rick B responded to my request. They simply decided after what seemed like hours of interrogation to leave the room with me trying not to piss on myself. I was beyond my limit. I sat in that stifling room with no window, my thoughts traveling at 1,000 miles per minute.

Eventually, they came back into the room glaring at me. Rick B said, "This is your last chance to work with us. Tell us who your supplier is or I'm going to see to it that your bail will be a million dollars. I'll see to it that you'll never get out of prison at least while you're still young."

Did he just say supplier...? Oh, heck no! I was shook. I started blurting out that I had always wanted to be a cop when I was a little boy. If they wanted me to work with them give me a badge and a gun and I'll go out and arrest half of Columbia! They had disbelieving looks on their faces.

I asked to go to the men's room again. I started feverishly moving around in the chair. Agent Black, an Afro-American was playing good cop, and Rick B, was the Redneck. Black said, "Okay come on, I'll take you."

He walked out of the room down a long hall to the restroom. When he opened the door the stench hit me. I wanted to turn around and just tough it out, but I had to go! Black guided me to the stall containing a small sink and a toilet.

I was still in handcuffs waiting to be freed so I could handle my business, but Black had other ideas. He said, "Go ahead," while staring at me! I said to him,

"How am I supposed to do this with my hands behind my back, tell me... how?"

He looked like I had just asked him a question about the solar system, like how far Neptune was from Jupiter. He did not want to take these cuffs off! He clearly remembered he was in the restroom all alone with me with no backup, just mano y mano.

I assured him I had no intention of causing him any problems. He finally took the cuffs off and not a moment too soon.

After I had finished, Black placed the handcuffs back on me. We went back to the room. I was expecting Rick B and Black to continue the interrogation but I was notified I would be leaving the building and taken to the Columbia, South Carolina Sheriff's department for booking.

"Aw man! It's on now."

I suddenly had a deep boyish need to call my mother. I just wanted to talk to my mom.

I was in shock after I discovered I was being processed. They took my fingerprints, photographed me and gave me a tight orange jumpsuit, I mean really tight and they ordered me to take a shower in an open area that smelled of mold and piss!

It was my first time going through this ordeal. I was exhausted and starving. I had not eaten in over 12 hours. I tried to convince myself that I was still dreaming, that this could not really be happening, not now when everything had been going according to plan!

Life Before Dishonor

My mind rushed back to before all of this chaos. Back on September 9, 2002, when I had just recently filmed my contract with Muhsin.

All I had to do is film the young men and women he sponsored showing growth and development in his M2 Foundation. It was a piece of cake. He had agreed to pay my company $350.00 an hour, plus expenses and 40% of the proceeds on the finish DVD production.

I thought about the television contract with Channel 21, which was going to air October 5, 2002. It was only 26 days away. I had the urban version of the Millennium Bike Show DVD footage ready for Platinum Disk, the company in Canada to sell as a dual package with the movie "Biker Boys." The release date was September 22, just 13 days away.

I had a contract with the biggest distribution company on the east coast, "UAV". I had negotiated with the president of sales who was willing to offer me Wal-Mart, Blockbuster and other video store contracts. He had big ideas for my Frozen Films Productions, ideas that I could work with.

I kept beating myself upside the head trying to figure out why any sane person would risk all of that for any reason at all. Especially, when I had a new woman like Sharon. I really wanted to get back to her. Everything was being flushed down the toilet and I felt powerless to stop it.

Animal Attraction

On September 17, 2002, I called Sharon from the county jail. She was very happy to hear from me. She assured me that she was going to do whatever it took to get her man out of jail. I told her that my bond was $1,000,000.

She said, "I'm getting you out no matter what it cost!"

I interrupted her saying, "Sharon, listen to me closely. I need you to do exactly what I say no matter what you hear me!"

I told her I wanted her to go ahead and move to Chicago to forget about me. She said,

"There's no way I'm doing that."

I had to cut my baby off because she wasn't in her right mind.

I said, "Listen, Sharon. Listen to me! I don't want you to contact me for any reason!"

She screamed, "Why! Why not?"

First of all, I told her I was set up and didn't want her involved. I didn't want them to be able to say we had concocted a story together and come after her.

"I'm going to trial and I'm going to beat this charge! I'll find you when the time is right! I promise," I told her!

I could hear her voice crack. She was used to getting her way. My plan was not what she wanted. Nevertheless, she said that she would obey my wishes. The time ran out and we had to hang up.

I called Karen's number. She picked up on the first ring.

"Hey Honey, I was just thinking about you! I just got off the phone with Danny and he said if I could come up with $10k cash and put my house up, he'd get you out tonight! I already called my mother and she's on her way to the bank right now!"

"Darn Karen, you did all that for me? What do you want from me?"

"I just want you to love me like you did the other night before this dumb mess happened."

"I know I can do that. I'm horny as heck just thinking about it. What time do you think you'll get me out?"

"Soon baby, soon as possible!"

I told her to make sure she brought me something to eat, I'm starving. Time ran out, I hung up.

I knew Karen was going to take an enormous amount of my energy later. I couldn't wait. I had been thinking about her for 8 days straight. I didn't care at that moment how crazy she was or who hated her. She was coming to get me out of jail and putting her $250,000 house up for that purpose. I was wholeheartedly ready for her.

*   *

By 9:00 p.m., Danny must have pulled some strings because they released me. When I stepped outside, Karen was nowhere to be found. It didn't matter. I was so happy to be out on the streets I decided to start walking toward Karen's. If the truth be told, as soon as I got outside I felt like hauling ass away from that godforsaken heck hole but I didn't. I kept my cool. I saw a guy walking with a cell phone and I almost strong-armed him to use it. I wanted to call Karen and tell her I was out and walking toward the highway. I explained to the guy that I just got out of jail and I needed to make a quick phone call. He looked me up and down with a concerned stare but handed me his phone anyway.

When I dialed Karen's number she picked up on the first ring as always. When I told her that I was out she responded,

"I know. I just got off the phone with Danny. I'm coming off the highway now."

Karen had a heavy foot and always drove too fast.

As I was walking down the street I saw a white 300 Benz coming toward me at top speed. It had to be Karen. Sure enough it was.

She drove right past me doing what appeared to be 90 mph in a 45 mph zone. I dashed in the street after she zoomed past me pushing dust in my face. I started frantically waving my hands above my head and screaming her name at the top of my lungs because I knew she was blasting that music.

At the same time, I started thinking they might try to pick me up for vagrancy next. I couldn't believe she drove right past me. I know she had to see me. I started to run in her direction. I couldn't see myself being left behind. Suddenly, her brake lights came on. I was relieved, a feeling of calm returned. When she spotted me she made a screeching U-turn and raced up to me. When I open the door I immediately became excited. Karen had on a see-through Victoria Secrets panties and bra outfit with a split in the crotch area. She looked sensual. I was surprised she didn't get stopped and charged with indecent exposure. If that had happened, it would have been my loss in more ways than one. She even smelled good. She had my full attention. I didn't ask why she was half naked. I didn't want to spoil the surprise. I felt butterflies in the pit of my stomach. She kept smiling and looking at me with passion. My heart raced. I knew if I started something she would finish it.

I wanted to wait until we reached the house, but I felt myself growing weaker by the second. When she stopped at the light before turning onto the highway, she kissed me softly on my mouth. She tasted sweet. I yelled, "Stop the car! Pull over!"

I couldn't wait another second. When we were finished, she held me and whispered in my ear, "Welcome home baby."

That's what I loved about Karen. She would do it anywhere at any time. I specifically asked her to bring food and this is what I got. Who could complain?

We arrived at her house on the lake around 10:00 p.m. I couldn't get over how peaceful it was here. She opened up the door through the garage. I followed behind her up some stairs to her bedroom. As soon as I saw that king size bed, my hormonal glands activated again. We stared at one another and raced to get undressed. I had to catch myself before I proposed to her just like the basketball player. I knew Karen would take my proposal of marriage way too seriously and I didn't want to get her upset. I don't think there's a word in the dictionary to describe the way she made me feel. I feared she felt the same.

The ecstasy, the ultimate, unadulterated, release she brought out of me.

I had never been put on complete lockdown before because of my independence. I always managed to find an exit. Things got so intense we both fell asleep.

When I woke by Karen's alarm clock at 5:57 a.m., I was expecting to hear music but her alarm clock rang. That was my first pet peeve. At first, it took me a moment to figure out where I was. Soon after I finally could visualize my surroundings. Observing Karen's reddish brown hair, I remembered she had worn me out last night.

I had to get used to getting up at Karen's house and playing by her rules. I had been there before, but it was completely different for me that morning.

I went to the bathroom to take a shower. There, next to a walk-in shower were 2 tree plants and a huge tub with a built-in Jacuzzi. Besides that, his and her sinks, or hers and his. I guessed I would find out which. Whenever we were both in the bathroom, I made a mental note to thoroughly check all the contents in her medicine cabinet above the sink before she decided to hide anything. I opened it and briefly counted the bottles. She had 7 and I found that to be a bit unusual. It was obvious that she had some kind of illness. Hopefully, it's something I could get rid of. I needed to know everything about that if I was going to live with her and be in this relationship. She was only 31. She did appear to be healthy.

I found my roller blades on the floor of Karen's walk-in closet and headed downstairs to the garage. I drove her 300 to the park for some laps before I had to take her to work.

Greg's Studio

I decided to stop by my main man Greg's studio. I needed him to work with me on my soundtrack for the latest footage I had shot before my arrest.

Greg was a white dude whose father had stock in the Lexus Corporation. He was substantially wealthy, a 21-year-old school teacher, who taught music in middle school. He had an awesome ear for putting tracks together. He was a white version of Dr. Dre.

Greg's dad had bought Greg a big house and a 2002 H2 Hummer to put in his driveway. Greg's house was his studio. His father had to approve of most of the people who Greg invited over. I had met his father, John Ryan in 2001.

Greg was helping me with the soundtrack for several different projects and his father wanted to meet the guy his son spoke so highly about. I had been shooting a video for some of the local talent using Greg's huge house for some of the scenes.

Mr. Ryan wanted Greg to take life as seriously as himself. What Greg wanted to do was to meet some of the hip-hop artists that I had footage of and some of the celebrities at the parties I had thrown.

Greg's mother was more laid back. She voiced her opinion in public if Mr. Ryan was around and you could tell by her vibe that behind the scenes, she was in charge.

Greg and I started working at 10:15 a.m. We had 5 hours to come up with music to incorporate into the footage. Greg had me listen to several new tracks. He smiled as he flipped through each one, nodding his head to each beat as if he really did have soul. I always believed that there was a black guy inside of Greg's body, an old black musician spirit who had come back to life and possessed Greg's soul. It seemed highly unlikely though because the dead are conscious of nothing.

Glancing at my watch, I realized it was getting late. I had to pick Karen up from work at :00 p.m. We cut our session short and agreed to hook up later on in the week.

The Counsel

I didn't like the idea of sharing a vehicle but it had to work for now. I'd rent a car in the next few days anyway. Besides, it made Karen happy to show her co-workers that she had a new man and he was on-time picking her up.

We arrived at her place. She started cooking dinner as I jumped on the computer and started making business calls. I was trying to get as many in as I could during regular business hours.

I followed this routine for a few days and then it dawned on me I had to take time to figure out how to get my personal property returned that the police had taken illegally on the day of my arrest.

I was mostly concerned about my Buzz Link (USB) Hard Drive, my CD Writer, my Recordable Rewriter and my Dazzle Digital Video Creator. Those items were a must!

Karen was searching around for an attorney to represent me. She had spoken to her aunt Gloria who recommended I give a John Ericson, Esq. a call. Mr. Ericson agreed to meet on Friday, September 27th at 2:00 p.m. I asked Karen to ask her aunt if she knew how much it would cost to retain Mr. Ericson. I didn't have any money at Karen's and I had to have an idea of what to expect. She grabbed me from behind, kissed me on the neck and told me not to worry, and to look in her closet at the top in the back for a black shoe box. I brought the box to Karen. She smiled. When I opened it my eyes popped. There was hundreds of Benjamins stuffed inside. This was no small shoebox. I asked her which bank she had robbed. She chuckled and said,

"I'll show you one day if you hang around long enough."

She did not have to ask me twice. I'm in.

Karen asked me did I mind if she came along to meet Mr. Ericson. I replied, "No, I don't mind at all." I had no reason for not wanting her to come considering she was paying.

Once we entered Mr. Ericson's office, I wished I had come by myself. It was like going to a nightclub in the daytime. His exotic staff included a secretary who looked and spoke like a Latina but had Chinese eyes. Several beautiful women walked around smiling as friendly as could be.

Karen was bent. She was screwed facing them all. I sat there looking at the magazines on the table in the lobby hoping Karen wouldn't start acting out and take her money back.

Mr. Ericson came out and greeted us with a handshake.

"You must be Mr. Jackson," as he reached out his hand to clutch mine while displaying all 32 of his extremely white teeth.

"Come with me, Mr. Jackson," he said.

I reached over to grab Karen's hand and followed Mr. Ericson into his office. She smiled because she knew those females were watching us on the low waiting to make their move. She didn't let anything get passed her. I guess it was her way of protecting her territory.

Mr. Ericson listened very carefully to my version of the facts. I explained how I had been set up and how I had been violated by the police, how they had taken all my property without a search warrant. And I told him how the police threatened me to set up my friend and associate Muhsin, to help myself. His eyes widened. He assured me that he was going to protect my interest and property at all cost, but he needed half of his fee upfront. He put on an Academy Award Winning performance. He deserved an Oscar convincing me that I had the right counsel. He said,

"If you don't want to go to prison and get back at those corrupt cops, I'm your man!"

I was relieved to say the least. Plus, I could never set up my friends; I'm not built like that. I'm cut from a different cloth.

I was smiling inside when I thought about Mr. Ericson only wanting half of his fee. Heck if he had asked for the whole retainer, it would have been okay with me. I had access to Karen's black box and my briefcase was loaded. I peeled off $8,000 from my silver briefcase. He stuck out both hands displaying his pretty whites.

I should have gotten a clue then when I noticed a gleam in his eyes as he counted the money. But I brushed it off. We shook hands and agreed to talk at a later date to discuss my options. Karen and I were hopeful as we left his office. We decided to go to lunch so we could chit-chat about our next move. Karen was holding it all in for now. Darn! Thinking about all those fine ladies at Ericson's office made me hungry. I know he had to be pushing up on his staff, ethical or not. I've seen his type many times before. Smiles in your face all the time he wanna take your place. A backstabber!

Chapter 3

Put Your Woman First

Cassandra called me at 4:30 p.m. Friday evening. She said she needed to talk to me whenever I had the time; it was kind of important. I had not seen or spoken to her since the day of my arrest, a little under a month ago.

I told her that my entrepreneurial spirit had not been shot down by all of this and that I would stop by her house tonight on my way to Greg's studio.

She was devastated by all the events that had occurred which sabotaged not only my life, but her life as well. I told her that I had to make a few more calls before 5 p.m. and I'd see her tonight.

It was funny to see Karen's reaction whenever I was on the telephone. Although she probably believed that I couldn't detect her insanities, she underestimated my abilities and experience. I was 11 years older than she was and very familiar with women's insatiable nature and insecurities. Her light-skin complexion seemed to get darker whenever she became angry.

Karen was driving. We were on our way to her aunt Gloria's. She'd set up an appointment to meet her aunt Gloria the person who had referred me to attorney Ericson.

Karen had told me bits and pieces about her aunt. I had mixed feelings about Gloria, although I had never met her or anybody else like her according to Karen's description.

Karen said that she was a wizard, a fortune teller, who was never wrong about anything. I did not believe in magic nor was I going to be a victim of a con artist and scheme.

When we arrived at Gloria's, a dark cloud hung over her house.

I noticed that there were no birds flying or any other insects or animals around. It felt spooky! When Gloria opened the door she looked like a real witch! I couldn't move.

I said, "Hello," and asked her to come outside to talk. Karen knew I was scared. Since Gloria could tell the future she knew I wasn't coming inside so she smiled and looked around.

She had placed 2 chairs and a small table already out in front. I stood there observing the table. I could have sworn I saw a small lizard or a bird's foot laying on it burnt by the sun.

Gloria said that Ericson was a very good attorney. With her help, there was no way I would do any prison time.

I thought to myself,

"This is just like one of the old con games I played in Brooklyn when I was a kid - Three Card Monte."

There was no way a person could win in that game.

I listened closely! Gloria said for a small fee she would give me all the details to what was about to take place.

Karen said, "It's going to be the best money you'll ever spend."

Gloria did not say how much she wanted and I didn't ask. Karen told Gloria that we would come back tomorrow. They hugged and I said goodbye.

On our way back to Karen's I started laughing after about 4 blocks away from Gloria's wondering if she could see me and hoping she couldn't. Karen had been silent anticipating my response and asked,

"What's so funny? You don't believe Gloria is the real deal?"

I said, "Please. Do you think I was born yesterday or the day before?"

Karen smiled and said, "You'll see. Gloria's the real deal and she knows everything!"

Karen's cell rang. It was Gloria. She said to bring me over to her house at 3:00 p.m. on Saturday. Karen informed her that we would come and hung up. I was nervous and introspectively worried, but I played it off by laughing repetitively. Karen asked if I wanted to eat out.

I said, "Why not."

She drove to my favorite Spanish restaurant where I took all my friends. I knew the owner from New York. His family business was just like being at home where everybody minded their business.

I had started going to eat there with Jamille in 1998. She had found the restaurant while she was looking for a new place to find good vegetables to eat.

I ate out a lot, mainly because most of my female friends were young and didn't know how to cook. All except Sharon, who cooked everything with love. She had me begging for her lamb chops and yellow rice pilaf.

I tried teaching Karen to cook, but it was a lost cause.

Jamille use to throw everything in one pan, put it in the oven and Walla! "Vitameatavegamin!"

I really was starting to miss Sharon. Compared to her, everything in my life seemed minor, less comfortable. All except Karen's "crooked uterus!"

Karen and I ate until we were so full we were about to pass out.

I drove back to Karen's. You know what happened next. We took off our clothes and fell asleep.

The next day we returned to Gloria's. I was still scared but decided to take a chance on going inside. We had stopped by a teller machine on the way over. I took out $200.00. I was going to see what that bought me before going into Karen's 'Black Box' in the closet. I wasn't about to be a sucker for more than $200.00. Besides, she was Karen's aunt and it seemed like she could use the money. Why not keep it in the family?

Gloria looked like she had been up all night. I saw a man walking around in the kitchen. I assumed he was her man and was taking the liberty of making himself something to eat. I couldn't blame him. If Gloria's cooking was anything like Karen's, he was doomed. Gloria got down to business. She asked me what I had brought her. I handed her ten, $20 bills which she put in her brassiere. We sat down. Gloria said, "You don't have to worry about going to prison. I'll give you something to keep in your pocket or I could go with you and sprinkle a little potion around the courtroom and everything will go your way!"

I surely didn't want her in the courtroom with me because it would've been obvious that I had brought a witch with me. The camera would be the evidence had anybody decided to review the court's footage.

Gloria asked me when I was going back to court. I thought maybe sometime next year. I really didn't know, but was hoping to gather my contracts before going. I needed to complete the soundtrack for the bike show and I had to make sure Muhsin's footage was completed.

I had already finished working on the first 5 episodes for Channel 21. Gloria told Karen to go to the pet store up the street and pick up a lizard, drop it off and she'd have everything ready for our next visit. Karen looked at me. I was frozen. I knew then that what I'd seen on the table yesterday was a small animal's foot. She had been sacrificing them. I suddenly remembered my mother telling me,

"Stay away from demons and people that worship the devil." Karen was in a rush though and didn't have time.

A week had passed since we'd been at Gloria's. I needed to go to California with film footage to be edited by a contact I knew from New York.

I already had an editor. I had met and hired him after attending a meeting at the President's house of the Columbia Film Committee. He was a professional. He basically photographed weddings and commercials. He had dreams of going to Hollywood! He was Asian and that was his dream!

Chapter 4

Same Old Stuff Just a Different Day
The Shift

Attorney Ericson called me. He said that it was imperative that I appear in court today. We had agreed that I would pay him the other portion of his fee upon the first day of my criminal trial. I asked Mr. Ericson what time I needed to get there. He said, "Right away or at least by 9:00 a.m."

I had an hour to make it back to Karen's 'Black Box' and put my suit on. I drove to a barber shop and paid the person who was next for his spot saying that I was in a rush and couldn't wait in line.

Meanwhile, Karen and I were barely talking cause Gloria was telling her all my business. On my way to Karen's, I wondered about the likelihood of her still being at home. I drove up praying for her to be gone and for that 'Black Box' of hers to be where I had last seen it. I walked in the front door at 8:15 a.m. When I walked in, it was extremely quiet. No sight of Karen. I ran upstairs straight to the bedroom closet.

Yes! The 'Black Box' was there. I slowly opened it to find the $100 bills totally gone. I panicked. After a brief pause, I called Karen. She answered on the fourth ring. Really unusual. I said,

"Hey Karen, where's the money that was in the darn 'Black Box'?"

She was bent! This was no time for all her attitude. She knew I had to meet Mr. Ericson!

I said, "Karen, you know I have to be to court in 20 minutes with the rest of Ericson's money! I told you I'd pay you back the $7,000 right after leaving the courthouse!"

I was sorry for how she took the way I was treating her, but I'm stressed out about everything. "And when you come home we need to talk."

Karen then told me the money was in the garage inside the third big box on the left-hand corner inside a Victoria's Secret bag.

I said, "Thanks," and hung up! It was over between us. I'd tell her tonight. I located the bag and counted out $7,000.00, took a 5 minute shower, got dressed and drove to the courthouse. I hated that I had to rush to fulfill someone else's demands.

The Court

I made it to the courtroom on-time by 9:05 a.m. Mr. Ericson, D.A. Blue, and Judge Eve were huddled at the district attorney's table so busy, that they didn't hear me come in. I couldn't believe my eyes and started to get angry. I decided to make my presence known by saying good morning in my strongest masculine voice! They raised their heads. Judge Eve jumped up and immediately walked away. The D.A. and Mr. Ericson went back into the huddle for a final play. I opened my briefcase to write down what I had just witnessed.

Shortly thereafter, Mr. Ericson walked over to the table where I was sitting with his pretty smile appearing when I asked him if I'd missed anything. Mr. Ericson said,

"No! No sir, Mr. Jackson. We were just going over other unrelated matters. Although I didn't believe him, I nodded in approval. Judge Eve hit the gavel and asked,

"Is The State ready to proceed?" The D.A. responded,

"No, Your Honor. I haven't had time to go over the details of this case. It was originally assigned to another district attorney and I really don't know much about this case."

Judge Eve asked Mr. Ericson his stance on the matter.

"Well Your Honor, I stipulate with The State. I have a motion here to continue this case until which time the evidence can be thoroughly reviewed."

Judge Eve checked her calendar.

"I have an opening on Monday, the 8th. Is that a good date for the both of you?" They both nodded yes! Judge Eve adjourned the court.

I was pissed! I could not believe that my attorney had just moved to continue after hearing The State was unprepared. "Southern hospitality!"

When Mr. Ericson and I walked out into the hall I asked,

"What did you do that for? Why did you give the District Attorney the edge? What's the purpose of knocking a guy to the ground if you're gonna help him up and dust him off before the fight is over?"

Mr. Ericson said that the D.A. could have easily filed a motion to continue. I replied that he should have argued that we had a constitutional right for a fair and speedy trial. My case had been on the calendar for several months and should be dismissed since The State wasn't ready.

Mr. Ericson glanced around to make sure no one else was listening to our conversation. He whispered, "I thought you needed more time to handle your contracts?"

"Handle My Contracts," I replied!? I counted out 20, $100 bills, handed them to Mr. Ericson, walked away and headed to the bank to withdraw the money I had just handed to the attorney to pay Karen back. I knew that money would be a big issue tonight once we talked.

As I was walking to my car, I thought about Jack. His reasons for setting me up! I remembered the day when I drove over to his shop. It was the beginning of May. I was about to get ready for the trip to Miami and get everything in order for Memorial Weekend. Jack had the biggest smile I had ever seen before.

He couldn't have been that happy to see me. I thought he was smiling because I appeared to be doing well. All the time he was smiling because he had plans to throw me to the wolves.

My cell phone rang and it was Jamille. I had almost forgotten about her. She started blasting me out as soon as I answered, "Hello, Frozen Films. How can I help you?"

"Heck with you and Frozen Films!," she fussed. When she was angry her baritone kicked in and sounded like a dude. She continued, "I hate you! You make me sick! How could you do this to me? How could you sleep with Karen behind my back?" Her voice was breaking up like she was about to cry. I became sensitive, I felt like crying too.

I really cared about Jamille. She was my favorite girl. I had to pull over because her words were blinding me.

I said, "Let me explain!" I did owe her an explanation. I continued, "I know how you feel about Karen but everything happened so fast. She put up her house to get me out. She moved all my clothes there. She came to pick me up. She was there for me!"

We argued back and forth for about an hour. I realized that although she had moved to Atlanta, we still loved each other. That made me happy! We ended the conversation by promising to stay in touch always no matter what.

I sat there for another 5 minutes before starting the car engine.

I thought about some of the special times we had. She was one of a kind.

Once I had taken her with me to pick up some film equipment at a BJ's Superstore. I asked her to wait because I had my laptop and other valuables inside the car.

As I walked up to the cashier, I saw Jamille standing near the costume jewelry case in front of the store waving me over and calling my name. "Juwan, please come see what I want."

I said, "No! Didn't I ask you to wait in the car?"

That's when she cut up! Screaming at the top of her voice, baritone and all.

"I want it, I want it now!," she hollered!

Everyone in the store stopped and focused their attention on Jamille. I tried to act like she wasn't with me but then she came over and took my hand and said, "Please!"

Everyone started laughing as I walked over. I asked the cashier to unlock the case to sell us the pendant so I could hurry up and leave.

When I came back to the store weeks later, the same cashier asked me where's my girlfriend.

I smiled and said, "I left her at home!" We both laughed!

I started thinking about how I would break the news to Karen tonight that I was moving out! I was convinced after talking to Jamille that it had to be done! I had to keep it moving. Jamille's promise to keep in touch was the final nail in the coffin so I had to deal with whatever Karen and Aunt Gloria has in store for me. Besides, I was fed up with all of it anyway.

I drove to the lake by Karen's and threw in that piece of cloth Gloria had given me as far in as I could. I started to feel better right then. I drove back to my mom's house to let her know I was moving in as soon as I talked to Karen.

My mother was happy. She'd thought I was crazy for moving in with her in the first place. I didn't dare tell my mom about Gloria. If I had told her, she would have started quoting bible scriptures galore. I would never have heard the end of it.

I could hear her now! "Demons! You been messing around with those Demons! Don't you know the bible says to shun anything that is not of God! Don't be bringing no Demons in my house!"

And, I would have deserved it. Every Word!

Chapter 5

Places to Go, People to See
Mr. Harvey

My trial date was closing in. I needed to make a trip to New York to visit all of my family just in case I blew trial. I also wanted to talk to my trial attorney, Mr. Harvey. He and I had been friends for at least 25 years or more. He told a judge that he had known me for 30 years and that I was like a son to him so the judge would grant me a low bond. We were very close.

A New York district attorney had told the judge that I was a flight risk living all the way in South Carolina. If the court allowed me bail, I would never be seen in this courtroom again.

I did not expect Mr. Harvey to respond by saying 'if Mr. Jackson does not appear before the court on his scheduled court date, you can lock me up in his place!' My mouth dropped. I took my hat off to Mr. Harvey for saying that. He was the real deal.

He reaffirmed to me that he had my back. He came off so smooth that I knew he had missed his calling by becoming a trial attorney. He would have been a superstar if he had taken up acting.

Riding Shotgun

I decided to get going to New York to touch bases with anybody and everybody I could just in case. My good friend Donna agreed to ride with me and help me with the driving.

She also wanted to get some legal advice from a lawyer. She wanted to find out how she could help an imaginary cousin of hers who was locked up. She really expected me to believe she was going all out for a cousin. It didn't matter. She was with me and he was on lockdown upstate.

Donna was originally from New York, but unfortunate circumstances forced her to make a move to South Carolina. Her large family couldn't keep her baby's father from trying to kill her or even worse, Donna ends up killing him to protect them. She always chose the wrong type of men. Every guy she went out with became obsessed with her. They would turn into a jealous maniac. They would become stalkers, wanting to inflict injury on anyone who got in between them.

Once I was at her house relaxing in her bed watching television when her phone rang. She signaled for me to be quiet so she could talk without him knowing that she had company. She put the guy on speaker so I could listen to him beg her for some attention. He started telling Donna how he was riding around all day stressing over her and how he could not get her off his mind. He don't even be thinking about other women. The guy had a Jamaican accent, but all Donna did when she heard his true confession was to laugh in his ear and tell him she had to go. Then she hung up on him. That's just plain old cold-blooded. I started feeling sorry for the man. She thought it was the funniest thing and so did I.

I had to admit Donna was eye candy with dough. She ran her own health care business that provided services for the elderly and anyone who needed help. She had around 35 employees. 'All Care Providers' was very successful. And Donna worked around the clock to keep it that way.

Big Apple

After 9 hours we finally neared New York. I loved coming back to where I started from. I checked my watch around 6:30 a.m. We glided through the morning traffic on the New Jersey Turnpike doing 80 mph with ease. The sun was coming up and God's creation looked splendid. The first order of the day was to get to my brother's, take a nap and a long hot shower to refresh myself before meeting with Harvey in Manhattan around 1 o'clock in the afternoon. Donna and I had stopped by my brother's house because he lived in New Jersey. I couldn't pass up on that love and hospitality. After kicking it with my brother, Donna reminded me we had to get on the road if we're going to be on time for our meeting with Harvey.

By the time we got to the restaurant, we had a few minutes to spare so we stood outside soaking up the sights of how things had changed since we'd been up here.

Inside, I noticed Harvey was already there reading a newspaper. We greeted each other with a hug. I was happy to see him.

He was all smiles as he asked where I've been. I told him I've been busy down south.

Harvey turned toward Donna and asked where did I find this attractive young lady. I introduced Donna to Harvey. I noticed that Mr. Harvey could hardly keep his eyes off Donna's body. I knew he loved young Afro-American Women, but he was making a fool of himself. The last thing I needed was for Harvey to get distracted by Donna's apple bottom when I needed his undivided attention. He had to help me once again to get me out of this mess I found myself in.

Harvey kept gazing at Donna's caramel 38 double D's beneath her skin-tight black V-neck cashmere sweater. I must admit she did have a lot of cleavage showing. She was banging!

As we sat down, I noticed Donna had a fan club around her, darn near every dude there was eyeing her. I was flattered. After the waiter took our orders for drinks and food,

I told Harvey about what I had been going through in South Carolina.

I could see that he was taking in every word to the point that he started to turn red and he seemed to be breathing harder. He was going into his zone.

Suddenly he banged on the table. Mind you, the restaurant was crowded. He began to raise his voice. I'm like dag; he's lit up from all those shots of bourbon.

He reached forward towards me and said, "Wait a minute! You mean to tell me I've kept you out of prison your whole adult life only to find you went down south to get caught up and to make things worse. You decided to trust a redneck lawyer! You didn't even call me when all this crap was happening! Those lawyers are all country bumpkins!" Harvey continued to say,

"Why didn't you call me first! Why did you trust them with your life?"

At that point, I began to feel sick because I knew he was right.

I looked over at Donna. She looked concerned. I guess she started to get scared over how Harvey kept on yelling and banging on the table.

I'd forgotten to mention to her how Harvey was an award-winning actor and how he was like a father to me. He had plenty of practice displaying his theatrics in the courtroom. I carefully listened to what Harvey had to say and then decided to relieve myself.

The Intercept

I excused myself to go to the men's room. Besides, this would give Harvey and Donna a chance to go at each other. Knowing Harvey, he's going to try and impress Donna with his 'Who's Who' stories and how wealthy he is hoping she will give up those digits for later use.

Knowing Donna, she would more likely pass Harvey her telephone number to stay connected in order to help her imaginary cousin.

When I returned to the table, I could see that both of them looked extremely relaxed as if they'd reached an orgasm. Yeah, they'd exchanged numbers.

Harvey told me to inform my redneck lawyer to postpone the hearing for another month so he could work his way up there to handle the case against me and bring me back home to New York.

I told Harvey I had already paid Ericson. Again Harvey's face changed. This time he wasn't acting. He shouted, "SO WHAT!" He asked me how much I had given him?

I reluctantly said, "$10,000." Harvey looked at me as if he wanted to put me over his knee and beat some sense into me but he said, "So what! That has nothing to do with me coming down there and bringing you home."

We spent a little more time together catching up. After we were done I gave Harvey a check for his consultation. He insisted I pick up the check for lunch. After we all left the restaurant, I felt confident everything was going to turn out okay now that Harvey was on the case.

The Reunion

Donna and I headed back to my brother's house to relax after that episode. We decided to nap in before heading to visit some of our relatives. When we woke up, I dropped Donna off at her sister's and I went to see some of my family too. They were happy to see me, but I could not bring myself to tell them that I was down south on trial and that it might be the last time they see me for a long time.

My heart was in pain but I didn't want to worry them so I kept my problems to myself. Besides, according to Mr. Ericson and Mr. Harvey, I'm sure to win this case hands down.

Gloria was calling me regularly giving me the 411 on how things are going for me in her crystal ball. She actually changed her prediction of how things would turn out. She started to stress me by telling me I was going to be found guilty and get a whole lot of time in prison, but I would not serve the complete sentence because I would start living my life according to Bible principles and trusting in God. God would begin to move on my behalf. She also said I would be rich once I got out of prison and to watch out for 'the man with the cane.'

I didn't believe anything she had to say but listened to her voice message anyway. I couldn't help but think about my mother. She tried her best to guide me in the right direction but I would not listen. I had a hard head. I had to learn everything the hard way.

True Confessions

Donna called me to see if I was ready to pick her up.

We headed straight back to South Carolina. Donna started out doing the driving and gave me her assessment of Harvey.

She said, "Harvey is crazy!"

When I got up to go to the bathroom, Harvey started telling her all of my business about all of the times he'd saved me from prison and all the money I owed him for all the discounts he had given me for covering my behind. He told Donna she shouldn't try to get her cousin out of jail because it would be like flushing money down the toilet. He also told her that if she was ever in New York again without me to look him up.

I smiled to myself and said, "That's my dad!"

Donna thought she was shocking me by telling me that Harvey had hit on her, but little did she know I would have thought it quite strange if Harvey had passed on Donna's succulent banquet. Besides, they were grown folks and Harvey was probably testing the waters to see if he still had it since he was pushing 60, going through his mid-life crisis and doing everything in his power to stay young and in the game.

Donna started telling me about her cousin and how he's serving a life sentence. How he had it treetop tall when he was out here on the streets hustling. She claimed I would have liked him. I laid the seat back, turned the music up and closed my eyes.

Chapter 6

Reality Check

After my weekend in New York, I was mentally and physically exhausted. As I was lying next to Karen, my mind kept racing over my meeting with Mr. Harvey. I should have taken his advice the first time around. He had never let me down before.

I carefully turned toward Karen to see if she was awake. She had her back to me and wore her granny pajamas, her way of telling me she didn't feel like giving me any. Little did she know, I didn't want none. I needed to talk.

It was only 9:30 p.m. in the evening. She had not even bothered to turn on the CD player or the flat screen. It was quiet. I decided to turn on the television and wake her up. I needed to get her attention. At first she didn't budge. Just as I was about to resort to drastic measures she turned around and reached over to hold me. At that point I felt like a nincompoop! Have I been played? Have I been reduced to sneaking around her house so I wouldn't disturb her? Look at me, I even had a problem jumping in and out of her bed.

I should have followed my first mind and started packing my things while I explained my decision as I headed for the door.

But nah, I was dragging this out by going around the bush. I knew it was like kryptonite.

I noticed she looked smug as she held me. At that point I turned my back to her. Her touch didn't feel right, it felt cold.

Suddenly she was wide awake. She sat up, asking me how things had gone in court on Friday before my trip. I told her that, that clown of an attorney made a motion to continue my case! She attempted to console me by rubbing my chest and assuring me that everything will turn out okay.

I wasn't feeling it. I told her, "I think I'm done."

She slid closer to me as I moved further away from her. She asked, "What's the matter?"

I replied, "We need to talk."

She moved even closer and asked, "Are you unhappy here?"

I thought to myself, "How did she guess?" Her question was extremely strategic. She was setting me up. The same way she used to trick her dumb jocks and real estate clients. She loved insulting a man's intellect.

"Heck no, I'm not happy here!"

"Well, why not," she asked? "I know you're hiding things from me about yourself and everything else and using Gloria to make it seem like I'm the one with the problem, like everything that has been happening is all my fault. And I'm sick and tired of all those pills you keep popping. It's making you schizo!"

Karen went blank. She jumped out the bed and yelled at the top of her squeaky voice, "Okay! Then where's my money?"

She said, "You wanna leave, fine! That's cool, but you need to pay me my darn money first. Then you can pack your bags and leave!"

I sprang out the bed, snatched my pants down off the closet door, dug in my pocket, pulled out a chunk, peeled off 20 Benjamins and tossed them on the bed.

She became eerily quiet only to realize that I'd only given her $2,000.00 instead of the whole ten grand.

She grabbed the money off the bed and held it up shouting, "Excuse me. You're $8,000 short...Playa!"

"I'll give it to you as soon as the bank opens up!"

She stood in front of the bedroom door.

"There's no way you're leaving up outta here with your stuff without giving me all my money! Pay up!"

I pushed past her. "I'll be up the street in the hotel. You can meet me there around 10 a.m."

She sucked her teeth, rolled her eyes and put her head down as if she was sad to see me go grunting bye, as I walked down the stairs toward the front door. She couldn't help herself when she shouted down to me telling me to leave her keys on the table on my way out. I wasn't feeling her nonsense. I ignored her and kept it moving.

I couldn't believe I'd broke the spell. I was liberated! I finally got up the courage to leave that upside down uterus forever.

That succulent bush wasn't worth the trouble.

I had to keep my game face on even though I was feeling rather hopeless at this point in the game. I didn't see many options.

I felt like the playa just got played.

Karen had won. It was her and Gloria's way or the highway.

Soul Searching

My life was deteriorating. Jamille was in Atlanta doing who knows what or with whomever. Sharon was in Chicago. Cassandra and Carolyn were in Cali. Marilyn was married with kids. Donna was focused on getting her imaginary cousin off Riker's Island. And Karen just kicked me to the curb… at night! This is off the chain! This was definitely a broke, busted and pitifully disgusted moment. I was falling fast. I felt dilapidated. So desperate, that I started thinking about the one woman who would stand by me in all kinds of weather. When I called, she answered. The only true Samaritan whose doors have always remained accessible to a misunderstood brother like me.

My mother! She is my heart! I thought just for a moment maybe I should work my way back to Karen's, but I hurried up and chased that treacherous thought right out my head. It was time for me to start following my instincts.

When I arrived at my mom's house, she opened the door and greeted me with a kiss and a big hug. Believe it when I say it felt wonderful to be held by my mother. At that moment I felt safe. Protected.

The first thing she did was turn on the stove to make me something to eat. She has always given me unconditional love. Whenever the street gave me a beat down, I would go to her for that nurturing only a mother can give to a man in order to get him back on his feet. I love her so much! I don't know what I would do without her. I was in a defeated place as I sat at the dining room table trying to think of my next move.

I started to smell the food she had cooked for dinner earlier in the day: candy yams, fresh green beans, collard greens, with smoked turkey, yellow rice and peas, macaroni extra cheesy, deep fried crispy chicken, potato salad and beef ribs drowned in barbecue sauce.

As she placed my platter before me, I thought "this situation too shall pass," now that I could console myself with my favorite comfort foods.

While I was eating she told me stories about my dad. She never missed an opportunity to drop some wisdom on me and she knew that the best time to do so would be while I was eating. She knew I wasn't going anywhere until I had devoured everything on the platter and that took time.

She told me about how they had first met and how tall he was. She was so in love with him before he left her for another woman. My mom wasn't gonna put up with all his extra affairs. It was either her or them.

As I tore through my platter, I thought "I've heard this one before," but I just listened. I knew she needed to say what she had to say to me.

She always reminded me of how much my dad and I were so much alike.

My dad loved my mother. He loved her so much that he used to beat up on all the others for not being her. He used to drink and think and before he knew it, that big fist was pounding on some woman's head.

He never hit my mother. He balled up his fist once, but her sharp tone made him think twice before striking.

My dad was murdered by one of his women. He had shacked up with her for over 15 years.

Iola took a lot of beatings from him. The abuse she suffered was extreme. He put her in a position that she had to react or she would have lost her own life.

He came home drunk one night, Iola was up waiting with his rifle within reach. She knew that once he saw it he would become violent. She wanted it to be over. She had enough of his coming home late, smelling of other women, lipstick and hair on his clothes.

When he spotted the rifle he stopped and said,"You got it out. You better kill me or I'm gonna kill you!"

I kept thinking about how I felt the night it happened. I was supposed to go over there so he and I could talk. I never made it because I, too, had been drinking and didn't feel like going.

I knew with both of us having alcohol in our systems was a bad combination.

When I got the call from my brother crying so loud that I couldn't understand what he was saying, I knew something terrible had happened.

Deborah hid my gun. She moved fast once I got up to go in the bathroom. When I asked for it she said, "You don't need it!"

I went over to my dad's. When I arrived the first thing I noticed was police cars, James Willis, Walter White and his wife Marilee. They were all close to my father. They all put their heads down as I walked up to them. Nobody said a word to me.

I knew then that the worse was about to take place.

I went inside his building, ran up to the second floor and banged on 2A. One of the police cracked the door. My brother was a correctional officer. He said, "That's my brother, let 'em in!" The officer opened the door and said, "This is a crime scene don't touch anything!"

As soon as I saw my father lying face down on the floor, I panicked. I grabbed him, flipped his body over and lost it. When the police tried to stop me, I tossed them around like nothing. My brother John had to help them restrain me. It was overwhelming. All I could think about was revenge! Somebody was definitely gonna pay for this.

My mom said, "You want some more Kool-Aid?"

"Yes please," I answered.

As she went to get the Kool-Aid, I started thinking about how much I missed my dad!

I, too, would put my hands on a woman if I felt she had overstepped my boundaries or went out of line. I had to have a variety of beautiful women and their feelings were secondary. Except, Deborah. I had never cheated on her. I respected her and I loved the ground she walked on. My mom had been telling me to settle down. For some odd reason, my mom's words registered. It must have been the ribs. I can't tell the number of times she'd warned me that how I lived would eventually cause me problems. I'd think it wouldn't go down like that, but this time I really heard her. It was time to learn from my dad's mistakes before I become a casualty like him - tomorrow's headlines. I'd walk away from Deborah if it seemed like we were about to go at it. I just can't go out like my dad.

Besides, my bark was always louder than my bite when it came down to women.

Falling

My mind kept racing after I began to clean up the dinner dishes. I felt confused. Why was everything falling apart? Why have all my girls flipped on me? Why am I here at my mom's house doing dishes again? Nah, enough of this, I have to bounce back, this crap is not for me. It's time for a quick recovery and procrastinating is not an option.

I had several contractual obligations to fulfill. I won't fail! I will push forward and succeed from here on out. I had to maneuver myself out of this phase, rehabilitate and facilitate the next chapter in my life. The only way to pull off this bold move is to "just do it!" All work and very little play. Yes, I had been here before, but this time was different. Not only was my company at risk, but my liberty was on the line.

I have never gone to prison although I've heard many horror stories before. My little brother John told me that "prison is like trying to crawl out of the bowels of the devil." After hearing that, I wasn't trying to prove him wrong.

I knew I had to contend with a few obstacles first before I could get back on my feet. One was Gloria, that diabolical necromancer.

I wasn't one for believing in voodoo, witchcraft or black magic, but I was starting to think there may be something to what Karen had said because strange things were happening.

I felt like somebody was watching me. I found myself looking over my shoulder and I really didn't know who or what I was looking for. I suspect it was law enforcers. It was creepy.

I needed to stay on top of my game by staying in shape. So, I would get back into rollerblading in the morning and then hit Greg's studio in the p.m. To cap it off, I'll hit the editor's house around 9 p.m. and then I'd work my way back to my mom's house.

I knew on Tuesdays, Wednesdays and Fridays I had to attend class for photography, editing and film production. I made it my business to volunteer to photograph shows for my classmates on Saturdays just so I could develop my skills.

It was exciting learning how to operate all the equipment.

Keeping It Moving

I had to come up with innovative ways to reinvent myself and my resources. I was determined to remain independent as possible and continue to pay my way through life.

I had my editor put together a documentary about a motorcycle stunt team with a Rock 'n' Roll soundtrack.

I knew this was a money maker straight out the gate. It was hot. Everybody was eating the DVD's up faster than I could create them. I was loving it! Things started to feel spectacular again. I was raking in plenty of dough during the bike rally months and sold copies to the stunt teams and the Rock 'n' Roll bands.

I took it a step further and started selling the DVD's on my Frozen Films website. By networking, online doors were opening for negotiable contracts with major distribution companies such as U.A.V., one of the biggest distributors on the East Coast. I negotiated with the president of sales! I was attending and working every bike show and getting rid of boxes of movies. I was in my bliss. A Canadian connection wanted to run my urban version of the Millennium Bike Show 2000-2003 with the movie 'Biker Boys' on DVD scheduled to be released in September.

My future was looking splendid, but I had to figure out how to get out from under those bogus charges. And shop around for a new woman.

I had a sudden flashback and wonder if Sharon had moved on with her life. It was almost a year since we had spoken to each other. I decided to be realistic.

Sharon was 50, beautiful and successful so why would she wait for me to get my problems straight? If I received some real time, would she wait for me to get out? I think not.

Maybe it was time to contact Keith! After all, he had set me up with Sharon. He was the main reason I met all the dimes I hung out with. We were like family.

I flashed back to the day when Sharon, Kim and Sonya, who were married to professional basketball players treated me to lunch on my birthday. That's the day Sharon and I became official.

When I arrived at the IHOP, there sat 3 of the most beautiful ladies I had ever seen. They sang happy birthday to me. I sat in the middle. We laughed and ate until it was time to leave.

Sharon slipped me her number. Later on that night she came over. She spent the night. The next morning I tried to rush her out. I didn't want her killed by her husband, but she refuses to leave. She said, "I was put on this earth to be with you."

I laughed uncontrollably. I told her that she was a player and that she probably said that to all her men or in her case, husband!

She insisted that it was true.

She told me that Keith had told her that I had plenty of women. She didn't have a problem with it. She said, "Put me on your team, I'll show you! You don't need them other girls!"

I had to give her a chance to prove herself. This was definitely my time to shine!

With a woman like Sharon, plus I had accumulated raw footage of rappers, R&B, Country, Rock 'n' Roll, singing groups, professional athletes, actors and entrepreneurs. You name it, I had it all.

The best part about it was I could get out there and take as much footage as needed and not get sued. I locked everything in by copyrights. I used legal waivers and release forms in all my footage. Covering my behind was the first goal on my agenda.

I had Baby Girl interview almost every celebrity I came across. She is beautiful. Everybody enjoyed talking to her.

They would give her their take on how they rose to the top of their game, their intentions about giving back to the community and being a mentor to the younger generation.

I decided to call my television show, "The Everything You Want To Know Show".

I created the website and email address using the name of the show with ".com" at the end so viewers could interact and provide me with feedback on how to improve my business. They could also find out where the next gig was taking place. I began to produce the shows according to the audience's appetite. I had an extraordinary chance of getting picked up by a major television station. I was determined to make my life work. As a kid growing up, I used to come up with all kind of ways to make money. Me and my friends sold TV guides, newspapers, gold, silver and we helped ladies with their groceries. We hustled. That's how we grew up!

Chapter 7

Preliminary Hearing

I woke up in a cold sweat feeling like an emotional wreck. It's September and my trial is about to start. I need to get to the courthouse and meet my attorney Mr. Ericson, so we can form a strategy since we will be picking the jury together.

I'm feeling helpless and dependent at the same time. I want to regain my independence, but I'm at the mercy of strangers who have never met me and who don't know anything about me. At the end of the day, they will be deciding my fate.

I rushed to take a shower and get dressed. I darn near twisted my ankle jumping into my Giorgio Armani two-piece navy blue suit, a snow-white Ralph Lauren button up shirt, my black Gators with a matching belt.

I made it my business to stop by my barber the night before to make sure my appearance was right. I have to make an impression on the jury that I'm an entrepreneur by trade, and not some lowlife drug dealer with no regard for life.

I keep trying to calm down, but I cannot help feeling anxious.

I slipped on my Rolex as I headed out the door. I arrived at the courthouse around 9:05 a.m.

I expect today will be a good day, but upon entering the room I noticed Mr. Blue, the Assistant District Attorney, standing at the opposite table with Mr. Ericson.

I greet Mr. Ericson just as Mr. Blue approached us to state that he will be introducing a tape into evidence for the prosecution.

I was horrified and relieved at the same time. I had no clue what type of evidence it could be, but he had to provide us with what he has since the information he has is considered discovery for the defense.

He was obligated to disclose any pre-trial evidence to us at least 12 days before trial. This bombshell is suspect to say the least. Mr. Ericson and I were shocked on the same page as we turned toward each other.

I started thinking to myself, "Awe man, it's on now!"

Somehow I managed to keep my composure and allow Mr. Ericson to earn his money by taking the lead as we follow the clerk to a side room to review the tape.

My attorney was still struggling to wipe that stunned look off his face. I had to nudge him and look as confident as I could to help him regain his focus. He looked like he was the one on trial and not me! Once the prosecutor entered the room, the clerk pressed the play button. It started out stating "This is conversation #1 of the CRI (Confidential Reliable Informant) and The Defendant."

"Yo Man, I'm gonna need both sets of rims. You hear me?"

"Yeah, I hear you. What time do you want to meet me?"

Just then I remembered Jack telling me he had to play it off like he was buying his wife a new set of rims in order to get out of the house. At the time it was no big deal. I didn't think anything about covering for him because we needed to stick together when it came down to our girls and in his case, his wife.

I didn't get a chance to respond because just as I was about to answer him, Carolyn had come into my apartment while I was talking. She had come without Saundra with an agenda on her mind. She was trying to work me over. She was working my zipper down as I was talking. I was telling her to stop while I looked at her with a serious stare.

Then I noticed the tape had been altered by another person's voice talking over my actual conversation. Mr. Ericson picked up on the flawed evidence at the same time as I did. The next part started, "This is conversation number 2 of the CRI and The Defendant."

The second portion of the tape was even more distorted than the first part. Everyone in the room except for the district attorney looked bewildered. We all started looking at each other in exasperation.

Though this was ridiculously funny, I could not break a smile since I was the unfortunate object of this bad joke.

Mr. Ericson seemed confident again as he turned to me and said, "Don't worry about what's on that tape. The jury will have to decide if they can decipher what's on it and if it's relevant to the prosecution's case against you. If we had a hard time understanding it, they will too!"

After reviewing the prosecution's evidence, we headed back to our table in the courtroom. Jack sat in the back of the courtroom looking scared to death.

The Choke Hold

Just as we were about to discuss our strategy, the court clerk approached us to tell us that the arresting officers and the district attorney wanted to have a word with us. The clerk led Mr. Ericson back to another room directly behind the courtroom with me following close in the rear.

When the door opened, I immediately recognized Mr. Tyrone Blue, the South Carolina District Attorney, the South Carolina police officer who concocted this farce Rick Buster, and A.T.F. Agent Carl Black.

Mr. Ericson leaned over toward me whispering, "Don't say a word unless I tell you to!"

Rick Buster spoke first. "Okay, here's the deal. We are willing to drop the charges and give you probation if you do not go to trial. You won't have to work with us if you don't want to. Just sign this sworn statement admitting guilt!"

I thought the D.A. was the person that made the deals happen not the police.

Anyway, I was waiting for my attorney to jump in. He didn't. So my temper started to get the best of me. At that point I was ready to bust him right in the mouth and knock his teeth out for trying to play me.

I couldn't believe that son of a gun was taking me for some idiot! He suggested I claim to be guilty to their setting me up and I don't have to work with them. Put my John Hancock on what? When Mr. Ericson saw the expression on my face, he quickly reached over and grabbed my arm and squeezed it giving me that "don't you do it" look.

I struggled to compose myself. This time I had to fight to regain my focus. I was flabbergasted. That idiotic proposal knocked the wind out of me. I started to sweat. This must be the reason they call this the "Dirty South!"

Against my attorney's advice, I could not resist asking the 3 stooges one last question. As I glared at the DA, I asked him,

"If I took your offer will I get my USB hard drive back?"

They all looked at each other as if I had something up my sleeve and looked confused as if there was a motive behind wanting my property back. I was getting pissed. Everyone got real quiet as if my question did not deserve an answer. I waited around for 10 seconds, all the while thinking how imperative it was to retrieve that USB. All my footage was on it and there was no way I would be able to fulfill my obligations without it.

I was livid and stood up to leave the room looking over at my attorney and asking him, "Are you ready?"

I walked out of the room and Mr. Ericson followed me.

As we headed back to the courtroom, I told Ericson to star jury selection. I knew I'd have a better chance with 12 in a box than with those sharks. He commended to me that he thought that I had made an excellent choice to not plea bargain if I'm innocent. "The officers had violated your rights when they gained entry into your apartment without a warrant and seized all your property. They know they really messed up on that point alone." That could be the reason why they had not answered my question.

Ericson went on to say that the Cadillac Escalade was not in my name. It was not registered to me. My fingerprints were not on the black leather bag or the plastic wrapper the drugs were found in. Ericson made me think that my trial would be a walk in the park.

I began to feel hyped. I was ready to bring those corrupt officers down, with Ericson's help of course. I still had that feeling of paranoia considering all I heard about the South Carolina Court System. If the law enforcers were confident in their hogwash, then how secure should I feel standing in front of a judge who was close personal friends with the owner of the vehicle where the drugs were found? Mr. Ericson made it sound like I was the man for having my girl Sharon and the judge on my team. My head was high in the sky!

The Anomaly

The only person to show up at the proceeding was Donna and Mike. I trusted them. I didn't bother to tell anyone else about the hearing, not even my mother although she kept asking. I kept telling her I didn't know. Deep down I really wanted her to be here, but I knew it would be too much for her to deal with. I had decided to man up and handle the situation on my own, for good or for bad.

Donna was well dressed while Mike was casual. Her business attire made her look even more professional. Ericson had told me not to tell a lot of people about the hearing. He said it would scare the jury. What sense did that make? None, and I didn't question him!

The DA's side was just as empty as mine except for a few interns scattered around and an elderly woman who turned out to be the DA's mother. The D.A. went so far as to introduce his mom to Judge Eve during jury selections. That was my first clue that there was something definitely weird going on.

I started paying close attention to what was happening in my face.

I could have sworn I saw the DA's mom and the Judge Eve sending subliminal messages to each other like they were plotting their strategy right before my eyes. All that stood out were their teeth as they kept smiling at each other for no apparent reason.

No one was talking. It seemed that they were blinking to each other, signaling one blink meant "spare him," 2 blinks, "fry 'em!"

All I saw was a chronic case of eye twitching going on between them. I knew right then I should have gotten some reinforcement for myself by having Donna bring her 3 beautiful daughters with her. I could have used them as some sort of leverage. I was becoming delusional. My mind started racing toward everyone who could help me with this case.

Mr. Harvey was in New York and they had rushed the trial so there's no way he could make it.

I even thought about Gloria's offer to show up. I should excuse myself and pretend to have to use the bathroom, head for one of the stalls to call Gloria up on my cell and tell her to catch a cab with the quickness and meet me with her bag of tricks.

I realized I was beyond desperate when I was willing to deal with the devil and his minion. After what I had just witnessed, I knew my goose was on a sinister rotisserie. Oh did I need a miracle to escape this fiendish plot to deprive me of my money, women and freedom?

Clearly, the D.A. and Judge Eve had no respect for an individual's boundaries and self-worth. If they could play dirty so could I. I have always lived by the code of a righteous man, "surviving" by any means necessary!

Mike sat there looking worried and more uncomfortable then I had ever seen. He really wanted me home too. He had invested a lot of time building my Frozen Films website and he needed me there to encourage him. Although he was gay, he still was significant and a main factor in my life. He was my little brother.

Purgatory

Day 2 of my nightmare. I was still churning in the belly of the beast. The D.A. called his first witness Alcohol, Tobacco, Firearms and Explosives agent, Carl Black. On direct examination, Mr. Blue asked to state his full name and spell his last name for the court reporter, please.

"Carl Black... B.L.A.C.K."

"What is your occupation?"

"I'm a special agent with the ATF."

"How long have you been employed there, sir?"

"Fourteen years."

"What was your current assignment?"

"I'm a special agent here with the ATF on the violent crime task force in South Carolina."

"Were you working in your capacity as a narcotics agent on the 9th day of September 2002?"

"Yes, sir."

"Did you talk to someone else about this case?"

"Yes, I did."

"Who was that person?"

"South Carolina police officer, Rick Buster."

"What was the content of your conversation with Officer Buster?"

"That he had been contacted by Mr. Jack Taylor and it appeared the Juwan Jackson was ready to conduct a transaction of drugs."

"So you were looking to buy drugs from Juwan?"

"That's right."

"What happened next?"

"We made arrangements to call Juwan, later."

"What time was the deal between Juwan and Jack, your informant supposed to go down?"

"A little after 6 p.m."

"Did you search Jack Taylor on September 9, 2002?"

"Yes, sir."

"Did you search his car?"

"Yes sir, I believe I did!?

"Did you find any drugs on Jack?"

"No! I did not."

"What happened next?"

"The phone call was made, everything sounds fine as Mr. Jackson was ready?"

"What happened next?"

"Mr. Jackson was ready and told us to meet him at the YMCA." Mr. Ericson quickly protested! "I object Your Honor. Unless Agent Black spoke to Mr. Jackson." Judge Eve answered, "Objection sustained."

"Agent Black did you learn that the subject, Mr. Jackson, was ready to go forward with the transaction?"

"I did."

"What happened next?"

"I notified other law enforcement personnel that were participating in this event. We proceeded to meet up at the YMCA."

"Did you see Mr. Jackson or a black Escalade?"

"I did."

"Did you see any other person fitting Mr. Jackson's description or any other black Cadillac Escalade?"

"No sir, I did not."

"Where was it positioned?"

"It was in front of the YMCA, I think it was backed in."

"At the time are you on the telephone?"

"Yes, sir."

"Who are you talking to?"

"I am talking to Jack Taylor."

"Did you ask Mr. Taylor any specific questions?"

"Yes."

"What did you ask him?"

"I asked is it there?" And he responded, "Yes it's here."

"At that point you have confirmation that the cocaine is on the scene? What do you do then?"

"I notified the other law enforcement personnel and they came and effect the arrest and secured Mr. Jackson."

"Then what happened?"

"Officer Buster searched the Cadillac and found the 2 kilograms of cocaine."

"Then what happened?"

"Mr. Jackson was taken downtown. I told Mr. Taylor to go home."

"Was that the extent of your involvement in this case?"

"Yes, sir."

"Lastly, do you see the person by the name of Juwan Jackson in this courtroom today and if you do, please point him out and describe an article of his clothing sir."

"He's the gentleman sitting over there with the striped shirt and what appears to be a purple tie with glasses."

Mr. Blue said, "Your Honor I'd like the record to reflect that Agent Black has identified the defendant in this case, Juwan Jackson."

Judge Eve, nodded her head affirmatively. Mr. Blue had one last question. He asked Agent Black if he followed up or did anything else in this investigation?

"I participated in the execution of 2 search warrants, addresses that were used by Mr. Jackson."

"Did you find anything illegal at either address?"

"No sir, we did not."

The D.A. Mr. Blue said, "I have no further questions at this time Your Honor."

My attorney Mr. Ericson cross-examined Agent Black.

"Good afternoon Agent Black."

"Good morning Mr. Ericson."

"Let's start with did you prepare a sworn statement in this case?"

"Yes sir, I did."

"Why?"

"Because some cases might take a year or two before they're tried and my memory is not what it used to be."

"How long have you known your informant, Mr. Taylor?"

"About a week."

"Did you mention that in your report?"

"No sir, I did not."

"Why not?"

"I'm sure I could remember how long I knew Jack Taylor."

"Was Jack wired prior to meeting up with Mr. Jackson?"

"No."

"Why not?"

"The only electronic equipment we had at the time was a phone to tape the conversation."

"From Jack's phone?"

"Correct."

"So, Mr. Taylor was not wired to supposedly meet with my client to make a 2 kilogram a $56,000 or $200,000 deal so you could bring it into this courtroom and show it or play it to the jury?"

"Correct."

"You don't have any phone records that show Jack Taylor had a conversation to a phone Registered to Mr. Jackson to present to this jury?"

"No, sir."

"Did you send it off or make any effort to test the bag for a fingerprint analysis?"

"I did not."

"Why not? Is it your testimony that Jack actually was in the Escalade with Mr. Jackson?"

"Is that my testimony?"

"Yes, is it?

"No, it is not."

"So, you never saw Jack in the Escalade?"

"No."

"As a matter of fact, he was coming from inside the YMCA, walking down the steps. Is that correct?"

"I didn't participate in that!"

"From your knowledge did you or any other agent or officer have any conversation with Sharon Smalls, the lady who the Cadillac Escalade was registered to?"

"No."

"I'm afraid to ask why not to that question."

I sat there in a daze as Ericson questioned Black. I could not believe the short answers Black was giving. He seemed confident that his answers satisfied the judge and the jury. I knew by the expression on the judge's face that she had already condemned me. The jury seemed to be following her lead. I am about to be bent over without any lubrication!

Chapter 8

Conspiracy Theory

Even the highest part of my thoughts was exiguous, I could not believe my eyes or my ears. If this eye twitching and line of questioning continued, it will be over for me.

The State was about to call its next witness. My lawyer was biting his fingernails all the way down to the cuticles while watching me with his peripheral vision.

Judge Eve, the DA, Mr. Blue, and the arresting officers were all free from any moral thoughts in most of the trials they were involved in. They all had personal, as well as professional agendas, that evidently had to be reached.

Jack Taylor walked slowly to the witness stand. To me, it appeared that everything was moving in slow motion. While I want things to speed up, I wanted everything that was happening to just stop! I had put too much faith in an over-paid attorney.

I now wonder what kind of personal agenda and scheme Ericson had. It seemed he was slowly undermining my chances of winning. My view of freedom began to dwindle right in front of my eyes.

Perjurer 2

I once heard that 'a lie is a lie, no matter who tells it!' The nugatory effect that it had on the jury was my main concern. The district attorney clearly stated, "Please state your full name and spell your last name for the court reporter."

"Jack Taylor... T.A.Y.L.O.R."

"Mr. Taylor, what is your occupation?"

"I work at an auto shop."

"...You used to also sell drugs, right?"

"Yes!"

"Did you purchase drugs too?"

"Yes!"

"How many times, how much currency exchanged hands between the two...?"

"Anywhere between $100,000 to $250,000."

I was wondering if a lie detector test can be brought in. Jack was lying through his teeth. He kept a straight face to the point I almost believed him. I couldn't figure out why they were allowed to question Jack about money they didn't have. I only had $85.00 on me at the time of my arrest.

"Come on Mr. Ericson, say something! Isn't it a crime to lie under oath?"

"What kind of vehicle did Mr. Jackson drive?"

"A truck."

"Did you know him to drive a black Cadillac Escalade?"

"Yes!"

"So you met at the top of the steps of the YMCA?"

"Yep!"

"Then what happened?"

"We just exchanged hellos, what's up man and he says, well let's sit… in the truck."

"So you then engage in conversation about oil-based and alcohol-based cocaine?"

"Yes."

"Why is that?"

"Just so I can have an opportunity to ask him to see the cocaine."

"Did he let you see it?"

"He sure did!"

"Then what happened?"

"I was on the telephone talking to Agent Black, who was asking me questions."

"What was he asking you?"

"Is it there?"

"By asking you is it there, what was he referring to?"

"The cocaine."

We were outmaneuvered by Mr. Blue's cleverly designed questions. By now I was considering standing up and objecting myself. Fourteen questions and not one single objection! What part of the game is this? What was I paying him to do? Just sit there and drink water or whatever it was he is sipping on.

Accuracy of Truthfulness

The judge said, "Mr. Ericson, it's your turn!"

"Thank you, Your Honor."

"Okay Jack, May of 2002, four months prior to your setup of Mr. Jackson you got charged with 2 counts of trafficking in cocaine. Correct?"

"Correct."

"Level 2. You face 70 to 84 months of each count correct?"

"Correct."

"Combined would've been 15 years. Correct?"

"Correct."

"You've already gotten one of those counts dismissed for your testimony here today so you don't face fifteen years anymore do you?"

"If it's dismissed, I don't."

"You don't know?"

"That's right. I know I can get time."

"You're not in prison, are you?"

"No!"

"You're still out."

"Yes."

"And you're still out here as long as you set people up. Right!"

"Wrong! I haven't set people up, just one person."

"You work at an auto shop, right?"

"That's true."

"Rims are part of a deal with cars. Correct?"

"Yes!"

"Say that you're towing somebody. You tow people?"

"Yes."

"So for a person that doesn't know what you're about and know that you're trying to set them up, for them to hear you talking about towing somebody or talk about car rims to that person, that wouldn't be out of the ordinary would it?"

"For people who don't know me, no!"

"It makes it easy for you to pull the wool over somebody's eyes when they know you deal in cars to come to court and tell him, No! That really means dope, right?"

"Wrong!"

"How long were you inside the Escalade with Mr. Jackson?"

"I'd say, roughly two to four minutes."

"And it's your testimony that at some point you saw the cocaine?"

"I said I didn't see the cocaine until he popped the back open."

"How long were you at the back of the vehicle?'

"Approximately two to four minutes."

"You realize that no surveillance officer says that they saw you in or behind that vehicle. You realize that, don't you?"

Mr. Blue quickly objected, Judge Eve sustained his objection.

Mr. Ericson said, "Nothing further, Your Honor."

Judge Eve asked the DA, "What about you?"

"Yes! Your Honor! I have a few more questions." Judge Eve said, "Okay."

"Have I promised you anything for your testimony here today?"

"No!"

"Were you ever in a black Escalade on September 9, 2002?"

"No!"

"Did you have a black leather bag that you placed into a Cadillac Escalade on September 9, 2002?"

"No, I did not!"

The D.A. said, "Nothing further, Your Honor."

I kept thinking to myself that here in South Carolina's court system, there must not be any penalization for perjury in State Court. Either everyone was dozing off or I was the only one listening. He just said he wasn't ever in the car on the day of my arrest. But earlier he said I told him to sit in the truck so we could talk. Unless I was misinterpreting his testimony or hallucinating, he was definitely lying. Jack was going far out of his way to get me convicted. It was a clear violation of my rights.

I glanced at the jury wondering if they had caught the contradictions or could read my body language. I must confess that over the past 2 days of my trial, I've come to the regrettable conclusion that this was an unfair fight of 3-to-1! Them against me. My lawyer, the D.A., and the Judge! I was on my own and did not know what to do. I paid Mr. Ericson $15,000.00 to throw me under the bus!

Chapter 9

Clerical Responsibility

Susan's tears were tears of joy. She had prayed hardheartedly for the clerical assistant position. She was now working for Columbia South Carolina Superior Court. The head court clerk, Mary Lewis, had chosen Susan from at least 100 other applicants.

Susan was special, soft-spoken and possessed a spectacular lethargic way about her. Mary felt it during their interview. She wanted to change her, make her into a model employee just like Denise and others before her.

Though the pay was mediocre, the benefits and working hours were a dream come true.

With a few weeks under her belt, Susan had already constructed a system to conduct her clerical responsibilities.

Susan reported any illogical matters to Denise who inconclusively looked into the situation. Mary had the final say. Denise instructed Susan to make daily morning coffee, pick up the post office box mailing and separate the attorney's briefs from the pro-se ones.

It was seldom that Mary required Susan's direct assistance. Susan recalled when Denise and Mary were put under pressure after an attorney alleged that his exhibits were missing from his brief which damaged his appeal.

The Judge at that time, Judge Myers, was furious because he knew the reputation and proficiency in which the appellate attorney filed his motions and petitions in the court.

He ordered the clerks to produce the missing exhibits within 30 days, or face sanctions for violating their clerical responsibility. Susan noticed Mary's nervousness more so than Denise's. Susan also acknowledged Denise's smile after directing Judge Myer's phone calls to Mary's office.

It was obvious to Susan that something extra on a more personal level was going on between Denise and the judge. Everyone in the office thought Denise was a loyal and happily married woman. Susan picked up on the truth the first week on the job after using her secret way of eavesdropping.

Her tactic was really quite simple. She would pretend to be listening to her MP3 player, rocking out with her headphones on while nothing was playing. She was an expert at it. She had been doing this for years and had heard more secrets than the N.S.A. Everyone in that office had secrets. Susan would probably learn them all very shortly.

She came from a low key, low-income family with 2 brothers and 1 sister. She was the youngest, the smartest, and the hardest working person in her entire family.

Susan owned her own car and condominium. She slept in the basement. Sacrificing was her middle name. Susan's trendiness wasn't in fashion but she knew how to save money.

Although she shopped at GoodWill and Salvation Army stores for her clothes, her appearance was always clean and fresh. She was very reasonable when it came down to things of significance.

She remained single for fear of dating a hoodlum or some kind of leech whose plan was to suck her financially dry. She wanted a God loving man. She prayed for that too. But she wasn't in any rush. She knew she had to be careful what she asked God for because he always seemed to act fast when it came down to her request. Susan noticed that both Denise and Mary seem to be atheists, but she didn't judge either and prayed for them both.

Mary and Denise couldn't put the blame for the missing attorney papers on Susan because she hadn't started working yet. As time went by, they both wanted someone else to shift the clerical responsibilities to. The true origin of Mary's work was hidden for internal reasons. Its magnitude is on a gigantic level, way above their understanding. It's a 'do as you're told situation,' Mary would always say.

Chapter 10

Malicious Prosecution

I remember Mr. Blue scanning the room. He knew he was in charge! If any of The State's witnesses decided to be truthful, maybe his dominance would change.

Judge Eve stated, "Call your next witness please."

Mr. Blue called S.L.E.D. officer, Rick Buster! My heart stopped beating for at least 10 seconds. I observed him very closely because he was the person who had violated me when I was arrested a year ago. Today he appeared strangely uncharacteristic. He looked soft, not so tough today. It was frightening but somehow libelous.

Mr. Blue led Mr. B as far as he could. He darn near answered his own questions without a single disapproval. My attorney must have dozed off again; I couldn't tell. Maybe he was waiting for the right time to strike.

Mr. Blue asked Buster several questions like whether he was working in his capacity as an officer on the 9th of September 2002?

"Yes. I was a sergeant, the supervisor of the operation."

"So in essence, you were trying to get the supplier?"

"That's correct. We wanted him off our streets."

"What happened next?"

"At the time some officers secured him. They arrived, they handcuffed him, searched him and I was handed a set of keys to the Escalade."

"And where were those keys?"

"I want to say when I first saw them, I thought they were on the ground. I think I was handed the keys by another officer."

"And at that point you find the suspect's cocaine. What happened next?"

"At that point, you can imagine that we created quite a crowd watching what was going on. We had a lot of officers out there. So we took the suspect and the vehicle. All of us took everything down to the police station."

"So he wasn't walking down the stairs of the YMCA?"

"No! He was running! He was attempting to get away!"

Mind Boggling

This is finally redemption! Did I just hear him correctly? Did he just say that I was running? Is he really talking about me, really? This is it - just the break in the case that we needed. Not only is this the most absurd lie of the trial, but the easiest to prove that the witness is lying. On the inside I'm bursting at the seams with excitement. I glanced over at Mr. Ericson who was furiously writing in his notepad. I couldn't make out his penmanship, but I am hoping it will damage the prosecution's entire case against me. I felt as if I was hyperventilating.

Up to this point, just listening to witnesses perjure themselves had drained my strength and confidence. All I could do was hope the jury saw this travesty for what it was.

They keep talking about the retrieval of some car keys to a vehicle that does not belong to me. Judge Eve looked disappointed.

I hoped she wouldn't call for a lunch break, an adjournment or anything that would give the D.A. a chance to regroup and turn the jury's attention back on me.

Officer Buster slowly dropped his head a little. He knew he had messed up with that testimony. He couldn't take any of it back.

I just hoped Mr. Ericson was about to step up to the plate and hit a home run. Mr. Blue said, "I have no further questions at this time, Your Honor!"

I tapped Mr. Ericson on his arm, smiled and whispered, "Do your thing partner!"

Judge Eve looked sternly at my attorney and said, "Your witness Mr. Ericson!"

"Did you prepare a written statement in this case, sir?"

"Yes, I did."

"This statement that you prepared, you prepared close to the date that these events transpired?"

"Within a week or so, maybe a little later."

"And your recollection a year ago as to something that happened would be better a year ago than now, correct?"

"It could be, yes sir."

"It could be depending on the answer you want to give right?"

"That wouldn't bother any larger scale deals. I recall them pretty well."

"This is a large scale deal, isn't it?"

"Yes, sir."

"Now, you said… to this jury that this man… I'm trying to find it here in my notes…because we almost jumped up and down over here. You testified that this man was running away as if to escape. Is that what you just said Sergeant Buster?"

"I believe so, yes."

"Where in your written statement did you write down that he was running away trying to escape, do you need to look at it?"

"No!"

"You know it's not in there don't you?"

"No, sir."

"You didn't write that did you?"

"No, sir."

"As a matter of fact, you wrote he was cooperative didn't you?"

"Yes, sir."

"And running and cooperation are not the same thing, are they?"

"Well, you're getting the two confused. When I saw him he was running away and I said I believe the second go-round. I'm pretty sure I said that he was not in a full run but quickly leaving the scene and when I came up he was very cooperative because I had my gun pointed at him and gave him directions to get down on the ground. So I believe there are 2 separate situations here."

"So he did something that was unique and positive when he cooperated?"

"Yes, he got on the ground so I didn't have to chase him."

"But nothing about running isn't that right?"

"No, sir."

"Nothing! But you're telling the jury here today all of a sudden now you're alleging he was running, is that right?"

"This is the first time I've had to tell this story."

"Well, it's not the first time you had to write this story or dictate notes about the story is it?"

"No, sir."

"In your statement, you stated that you were the closest person to the suspect and you said that he was near the front hand side or the business, correct?"

"Correct."

"You didn't say he was near the Escalade did you in your statement a year ago when this was fresh on your mind?"

"You need to repeat that."

"Sir I'm basing these questions on your statement."

"Let me see it! Okay."

"Do you need an opportunity to look through that?"

"No, sir."

"Sergeant was the closest to the suspect, near the front right-hand side of the business. Is that right?"

"That's correct."

"No audio or video equipment was used by any enforcement officers at any point during these proceedings, correct?"

"No, sir."

"And you're telling the citizens of South Carolina that our police department can't do that because the audio equipment is not any good and because the video equipment is not that good?"

"No, I mean, I didn't say that."

"When did you first see Jack Taylor on September 9th, 2002?"

"I never saw him at all."

"You never saw him at the YMCA?"

"No."

"So you don't know from your own personal knowledge of what you saw, whether he was even there or not. Is that what you're telling the jury?"

"I was in contact every moment with Agent Black and I relied on Agent Black to provide me with the details of the events that was his part. He was with Jack, and Jack was on the scene. I did not see Jack."

"As the supervisor in charge of this operation you did not submit the black leather bag or the black garbage bag to any laboratory in this city or state for analysis, did you?"

"No."

"Prior to Friday, before Monday of this event, did you know Jack Taylor?"

"No sir, I did not."

I was thinking about how Jack could be a CRI if none of the officers or agents knew him before last week. Jack couldn't have been a "Confidential Reliable Informant!" Jack had tricked, coned, duped, hoodwinked the police all in a week. He fooled them into committing felons. Obtaining property by false pretenses and making false, written, and verbal statements. Jack had them and me right where he wanted.

Chapter 11

Perjure #3

At this stage of the trial, I knew we were gaining some ground for a mistrial or an interlocutory appeal. A few legal questions had to be decided before this case could become final. The informer, as well as several other State witnesses had clearly committed perjury, and presented misleading contradictory and verbal written statements. These injurious falsehoods not only damaged my chances to regain my liberty, it also created an unnecessary hardship for my family.

In no way could the D.A. recant the witnesses previously made statements without admitting to their untruthfulness. So he had decided to call a State Bureau of Investigation agent to the stand. His intentions were to use the S.B.I. agent's credentials as credibility. His variety of tactics was carefully planned.

Mr. Blue stood up proudly and said, "The State calls Tyrone Spann."

Tyrone approached the bench. His personality filled the room. The only thing missing was a lorgnette. His neatly combed reddish hair gave him the appearance of messianic likeableness. I stared at him with a fixed gaze, stunned for 2 reasons.

My attorney was swiftly thumbing through his thin pieces of papers. I didn't want to disturb him but I had no choice! At my first tap he didn't respond. So I waited a few more seconds. The D.A. asked his first question.

"What was your current assignment on or about September 9, 2002?"

"My current assignment was clandestine lab or methamphetamine lab coordinator for the western part of the state."

"What does that mean in layman's terms for the jury?"

"I go around with the S.W.A.T. team and we raid the methamphetamine labs, the clandestine labs around the state and then control the cleanup of them, the arrest of the people inside and the process, you know the clandestine labs."

I elbowed my attorney a little harder this time. He looked at me then asked, "What is it?"

I replied, "That guy wasn't even there. How does he get to testify?"

"Are you sure?"

"Yes, I'm sure. Just ask him how he knew about my arrest?" My attorney nodded and took a long sip of water. The D.A. continued...

"And how many times would you estimate that you've seen drugs in Columbia or in any part of the state?"

"In the hundreds."

"Have you ever had to pose as an undercover buyer and did you see Jack and Juwan get out of the Cadillac Escalade?"

"Yes to both questions."

Mr. Ericson said, "Objection, Your Honor! I'm going to object and be heard outside the presence of the jury."

Judge Eve calmly said, "All right ladies and gentlemen, back into your jury room please for a few minutes."

"Okay, go ahead Mr. Ericson."

As the door closed Ericson said, "Your Honor, the basis of my objection is that I believe that The State has failed to comply with the discovery request and I believe you have the court file or the clerk has the court file. I filed a motion for discovery quite some time back. I saw that this Agent Spann in the courtroom, was not familiar with him and I'm not familiar with all the officers who work these cases. But when I heard the name Tyrone Spann and I looked, I have no written statement from this officer. I have nothing in discovery about him indicating in any way that he was involved in this case. My client doesn't remember seeing him at his arrest. And I find it somewhat convenient that so far no officer sees anybody getting out of the vehicle. They're all in similar positions. Now we've got this person who I have no statement from, who is going to come in here and try to testify to that issue. The State has failed to disclose this person as a witness. I don't know whether he's produced a statement to them or not on these matters and since they failed to disclose him. I don't think his testimony should be allowed."

Jude Eve hesitated for a brief moment. She turned her nose up at Mr. Ericson and said, "Mr. Blue!"

"Well Your Honor, speaking very specifically to the inquiries, the first answer is no. We do not have a statement from Officer Spann. He is, however, listed on the statement from A.T.F. Agent Black as one of the participants or one of the individuals who is present. I don't have his statement. Mr. Ericson would not be entitled to it under the Statue until after Mr. Spann testified in court as to his finding. There has been no unfair surprise here. And even if I did have a statement in my hand, it's here in Columbia, South Carolina, that we give everybody the statements, the labs we gave them all that at the first setting."

The D.A. made his statement without thinking it through.

I didn't know what it meant and it sounds like hogwash to me. Even Judge Eve had a fixed stare.

She said, "Anything further, Mr. Ericson?"

"It's ironic that every other officer involved in this case has a prepared statement. The one officer who's going to have carte blanche to get up there and have a say in this matter to cover up whatever's missing in The State's case is going to be an agent who has no statement and has a bare connection in this case.

I do claim surprise because I'm sitting here writing his name down and my client is breaking my ribs with his elbow to tell me he doesn't remember seeing Agent Spann at his arrest. Even if he doesn't have a statement, there's usually a statement in the discovery that says this officer did this task, that officer recovered drugs, that officer arrested the defendant, this officer was assigned to watch the informant. I know nothing about this agent. And it has affected Mr. Jackson sitting here looking at everything. I have prepared questions for everybody except this gentlemen."

Judge Eve gave Ericson a look that could kill.

"Mr. Ericson, if your request is to have me strike the officer or agent's testimony, then that request is denied! Bring the jury back in."

She told the D.A. to continue…

"Thank you, Your Honor."

"Agent Spann, I left off by asking you what did you observe when you got into position to conduct surveillance?"

"After they got out the vehicle, they went around to the back. Once they got around the back of the vehicle, the back end opened, then the officers moved in and conducted arrest procedures."

"And I asked you before, you saw Jack Taylor get out of the vehicle with Juwan?"

"Yes!"

"And for the record do you see Juwan Jackson in this courtroom today? Could you point him out and describe an article of his clothing?"

"He's sitting right over there wearing a purple tie and glasses."

"And this is the person you saw get out of the driver's seat of the black SUV?"

"Yes, that's him."

Mr. Blue said, "Nothing further for this witness, Your Honor."

Judge Eve smirked and said, "Your witness, Mr. Ericson."

He stood up and smiled. "Mr. Spann, you never produced anything to the district attorney's office?"

"No, I did not."

"You just happened to be in the courtroom earlier when I was asking Mr. Taylor about anyone witnessing him behind that Escalade, correct?"

"Yes, I was."

"Were you also here earlier when Officer Buster who was on surveillance and Agent Black said that they didn't see any activity behind the black Escalade?"

"I was here for Agent Black's testimony, but I was not here for officer or Agent Buster's."

"Wouldn't it be fair to say that your role in this was minor?"

"Yes, sir."

"Nothing further Your Honor!"

Mr. Ericson didn't have any more questions, but I had plenty. The Judge told Mr. Spann to step down. The D.A. asked the judge to excuse Mr. Spann for the day. She did.

Agent Spann, without justification, committed an act that otherwise would be a tort, a breach of duty, a crime in any other State in the world, without sacrificing any logical relevance.

I couldn't help thinking, this guy is ruthless. My gut feeling was telling me to get my passport and leave the country. What was he getting out the deal or was this routine? Did the D.A. knowingly put him up on the stand to purposely cause the jury to believe that I had domination and control over that vehicle? I was losing it.

My attorney didn't seem to have an answer for these out-of-place, bizarre tactics. The judge had abused her discretion by letting Agent Spann testify without preparing a written statement for my attorney to question him. It is still unclear to me how he came to know about my arrest. I'm sure he wasn't there. I would have remembered his red hair! Who told him about my arrest? He said he got a telephone call from Agent Black 15 minutes beforehand asking him to help do surveillance. All my attorney had to do is check their phone records and bingo! He's busted!

All I knew is I wanted him back up there on the witness stand. The jury looked satisfied. They had heard enough. I was another notch under the DA's belt. He stood there with his hands folded, twiddling his thumb, savoring the sweet taste of victory as if it was paramount!

Judge Eve's dishonesty was the final nail in my coffin. She knew what the law required, but she chose loyalty to Sharon.

If the truth be told, I would have probably done the same thing for my friend, if I had any.

Chapter 12

Pro Se Department

Denise had just hung up the telephone. Susan came with a stack of papers in her hands. She saw Denise's brief smile fade as she waited for Denise to ask about her plans for the weekend. Susan knew it was coming and knew that smile. Denise has once more plans again with the married judge who she had started an affair with a year ago.

Denise thought that no one suspected anything because she always bragged about how great her husband Tim was.

A well-planned misconception. Everyone seemed to believe it because Denise worked so hard and never seem to have time for anything besides Bingo on Saturday nights.

Susan returned the smile, but couldn't resist putting Denise on the spot by asking her about the missing attorney's papers. Was Judge Myers still pissed off?

Denise played it cool as always by mentioning Mary's name, stating that she handled proprietary functions with the Judge Myers personally.

Susan knew better. Nevertheless, she acted dumb as usual.

She hated Bingo and thought it was a big waste of time. The papers she carried came from the post office box which overflowed daily.

Pro-se post-conviction were serious business. Most of them were from recidivist offenders who were very familiar with post-conviction procedures, but were completely unaware or concerned about clerical responsibilities and the judges whose name appeared on the denials of their motions for relief.

They were totally in the dark as to who Mary, Denise, and Susan were, and the vital role they played.

The inmate law library, by and through carefully planned judicial discretion, was dismantled starting from July 1988 to January 1989. Although it didn't stop the continuing flow of Pro-Se Motions that were filed, it slowed down the accuracy of statutes cited by the inmates. It also took away all affirmative defense arguments needed to rebut any ambiguous motions to dismiss filed by a State District Attorney.

Mary has 15 years in by this time and saw the system's legal department dismantled and reconstructed with the regretful assistance of the Public Defender's Office.

The inmates were also unaware about the "rubber stamps" that the clerks used showing that a judge had denied the motion. Although many suspected something wasn't right, without any proof it was business as usual.

Legal ethics wasn't an issue to Mary or Denise. Soon, Susan would have to knowingly cross the line of legitimate superiority if she wanted to stay in that office.

Denise knew it was time to introduce Susan to the "rubber stamp." She kept it locked in a metal box in the bottom drawer of her desk and always wore the key around her neck on a thin gold chain the judge had brought her the 7th time she met him for coffee in his chambers.

Denise hoped Susan wouldn't ask any questions, but was prepared if she did. Denise motivated Susan to use the stamp by her influential awful remorseful storyline of how and why the lady before she was terminated.

"I can finish the rest of those if you want," said Susan.

"I already finished separating the attorney briefs from the pro-se ones."

"Good," Denise replied. Just make sure to stamp the judge's name on these!"

"I got it."

Denise watched for a short time and walked away.

"I'll be back in a little while. If you finish before I do, be sure to put the stamp in the box and lock it. Thanks."

Susan now took a deep breath. Although the conspiracy hadn't legally attached to her, Susan knew that it was about to be introduced. All Denise had to do was explain why she was separating those documents and stamping the judge's name on them and it was a done deal. One act of conspiracy to another. Susan stamped away. At 2 p.m., she decided to call her sister in Charlotte not to tell her that she was visiting this week, but to ask for information from the family attorney just in case his assistance was required. She knew that her sister would ask a thousand questions before giving her the number. The simplest response would be "realtor problems" from a tenant renting her condo in Charlotte. Susan's sister hated attorneys and would only use one as a last resort.

Susan briefly scanned through some of the pro-se motions that she had stamped Judge Myers' name on and couldn't see why they were supposed to be denied. The only relief the defendant was asking for was that the court reconsiders sentencing guidelines since the existing sentencing system resulted in serious inconsistencies between the sentences imposed by the judge, which violated the Sentencing Reform Act of 1984.

The motion wasn't asking for a million dollars or to be released immediately. It asked the court to correct an error or modify the sentence, general law that applied to all people in the circumstances described in the statute.

Mary opened the door, coffee cup in hand and headed directly for Denise's desk. Susan didn't see her approaching.

She dropped the unstapled petition to the floor.

"I'm sorry Susan," Mary replied as Susan knelt down to retrieve the scattered legal papers.

"Where's Denise?" Using her militant tone for having to apologize a moment earlier.

"She's somewhere around here. I'm completing this stack of documents for her."

"I see... Let me take a look at those."

Susan up and passed the papers to Mary. Mary went straight to the page reflecting Judge Myers name. It had been stamped, which brought a smile to her face. She handed Susan the documents back and nodded, whispering,

"Very good. Carry on and tell Denise to meet me in my office directly."

"Yes ma'am," Susan replied. Her soft tone let Mary know she still possessed the pivotal skills of intimidation. She walked swiftly away toward the coffee machine.

Everyone in that office walked lightly around Mary, except for Denise, who respected her and desperately wanted to replace her one day.

With her having Judge Myers and Mary's position, there would be no stopping her!

Chapter 13

Tainted Jury

The jury would not even look at me. The liberating chance of victory became crystal clear. I had missed the opportunity to leave the country. No more lunch breaks or other delaying tactics were available. I sat there like a mosquito waiting to be swatted. The monstrous outcome was real.

Two hours ago, Mr. Ericson had assured me there would be no prison time.

I quickly scanned the courtroom. Everyone ignored me. No one would make eye contact. The judge smiled at me without looking at me, tilting her head slightly to the left at an angle. I could see her moist lips turned up. I wanted to flip the table over. The positive side of my conscience broke out into "I'm innocent I tell you! I'm not a drug dealer. You should've locked up Jack, not me! How did I end up in this kangaroo court? This is a big mistake!"

Silence! They all had the duty to speak up but didn't. My attorney, the D.A. and Judge Eve, they all knew that this trial was a prejudicial judicial error and a miscarriage of justice. They would be liable if their actions were reviewed.

"Bring the jury back in," The judge shouted!

I remembered Judge Eve saying,

"Alright members of the jury, all the evidence has been presented and it's now your responsibility to decide from the evidence what the facts are. You must then apply the law which I'm about to give to you. It is absolutely necessary to understand and apply the law as I give it to you, not as you think it is or might like it to be. This is important because justice requires that everyone is treated in the same way and have the law applied to them. The Defendant has entered a plea of not guilty. The fact that he had been indicted is not evidence of his guilt. Under our system of justice, when a person pleads not guilty, he is presumed to be innocent. The State must prove to you that The Defendant is guilty beyond a reasonable doubt. In this case, you are the sole judge of the credibility of each witness. You must decide for yourselves whether to believe all, part or none of what a witness has to say. You should apply the same test of truthfulness as you would to your everyday affairs."

These jury instructions sound like crap considering none of them have ever dealt with an oil spill like Jack.

She continued,

"There are 2 types of evidence from which you may find the truth, as to the facts of a case. There is Direct Evidence and there is Circumstantial Evidence. Direct evidence is the testimony of a person who asserts actual knowledge of a fact, such as an eyewitness. Circumstantial evidence is proof of a chain or a group of facts and circumstances indicating the guilt or innocence of the defendant. In this case, The Defendant has not testified and our laws give him this privilege."

Hold up! Is this where I'm supposed to say something? I looked at Mr. Ericson. He had a warm comfortable look on his face as if he were relieved that I sat still and didn't cause an outburst! Judge Eve cleared her throat and said,

"The same law also assures him that his decision not to testify creates no presumption against him, therefore, his silence should not influence your decision in any way. The Defendant has been charged with trafficking cocaine, which is the unlawful possession of 400 grams or more of cocaine. For you to find The Defendant guilty of this offense The State must prove 2 things beyond a reasonable doubt. First that The Defendant knowingly possessed cocaine. A person possesses cocaine if he is aware of its presence and has both the power and the intent to control the disposition or use of the substance. Secondly, that the amount of cocaine which the defendant possessed was 400 grams or more."

I racked my brain to recall the first part of the Judge's jury instructions.

The judge continued saying, "If you find from the evidence beyond a reasonable doubt that on or about the alleged date The Defendant knowingly possessed cocaine and that the amount which he possessed was 400 grams or more, it will be your responsibility to return a verdict of guilty. If you do not so find or have a reasonable doubt as to one or more of these things, it will be your responsibility to return a verdict of not guilty."

She's basically telling the jury that the stuff is mine! Why isn't my attorney saying anything? Is he in a coma? Is he drunk? I should hit 'em with a quick elbow! As my mind continued to play tricks on me,

she blurted out more leading jury instructions. "If you find beyond a reasonable doubt that a substance was found in a certain place whether or not he owned it, this would be evidence that he had the substance and had the power and intent to control its disposition or its use. A verdict is not a verdict until all 12 jurors agree unanimously as to what your decision shall be. At this point, you may retire for your deliberation."

The jury walked out. I couldn't help feeling like the judge had just swindled the jury into sealing my fate.

"What does she mean it didn't matter whether or not I owned it? I didn't own any of The State's evidence! I had $85.00 in my pocket. I didn't even have the keys to Sharon's Cadillac. I couldn't be in control of the cocaine without the darn keys!"

The jury exited the courtroom and The Court took up other matters. I sat there heartbroken. Ericson faced me slightly without saying a single word.

A note from the jury asked where the keys were, could they have an inventory list of the evidence and could they see the pictures again? The judge asked the D.A. if there was an inventory listing the evidence?

The D.A. played dumb as if the question was not clear.

He replied, "Do you mean on one of the exhibits?"

She answered, "Yes!"

Mr. Ericson jumped in to say, "I think I had it and I threw it away. Judge Eve, I have a concern with them having an inventory. An inventory list was not put into evidence and I don't think it should be provided now."

Judge Eve replied, "And you don't object to them seeing the pictures when they come out?"

"I don't but where are the keys?"

That was a key question! Everybody looked dumbfounded. Judge Eve asked, "I don't assume that they're listed on the property sheet are they?"

Mr. Ericson jumped up and said, "I think there are no keys in evidence. I don't think the car was in evidence either! We heard testimony about keys being handed to Officer Rick Buster by ATF Agent Black, but no keys had been submitted to the jury or put into evidence."

Judge Eve asked, "You argued something about keys didn't you?"

My attorney whispered, "No."

Mr. Blue turned purple while saying he didn't remember anything about keys in evidence either.

I smiled for a brief moment because the truth was finally coming out. Just as I started feeling a bit of relief, Judge Eve stated, "No, there wasn't! I think that the keys were found on the ground after he was cuffed."

"Well Your Honor, I think that's one where the jury is going to have to recall the evidence of the case."

Nonsense! Without those darn keys, no other evidence links me to the SUV or the 2 kilograms of cocaine.

Here I am being tried without evidence and the court doesn't have a problem with the insufficiencies of the evidence.

Judge Eve decided to proceed. "So you think I should tell them that the keys are not in evidence and they will have to recall the testimony of the witnesses and the case."

"Yes, Your Honor." Both stated at the same time, without blinking.

She yelled, "Bring them back in!"

The jury came back in and appeared confused. Judge Eve asked, "Is there anything else and have you selected your foreperson?"

Joor #12, Mrs. Griffin, stood up and asked the judge is it too late to listen to the tape again.

The audio tape was replayed. Judge Eve asked if there was anything else.

"Can we hear that last part again?" The last part was played again. "Let me ask you this before you go back in. It is 12:00 p.m. Do you all want to work through lunch, or stop at 12:30 p.m. and then come back at 2 o'clock and finish?"

Mrs. Griffin said, "We'll work through lunch."

I thought that was a good sign, I guess. The Judge said, "Okay!"

The court received another note from the jury requesting to hear the second part of the tape and hear the definition of both charges again. They also wanted to get closer to the tape player. "Alright!" She impatiently said with a lot of bass in her voice.

I thought it was a great idea. Could it be possible that the jury detected flaws in The State's altered evidence? Or could they hear me in the background telling Carolyn to stop while I was on the telephone? Either way, it had their attention and I was glad about that.

My attorney wasn't saying much. He actually had a frightening look on his face as if he was afraid of something being revealed, something that we missed.

The jury returned to the courtroom. To my surprise, the jury had decided on one of the charges, but are 11 to 1 on the other and can't agree. Mr. Ericson said, "I think that's where we have the pattern instruction, the Allen Charge. I have a copy of it."

"Is that failure to reach a verdict," Judge Eve whispered?

Ericson said, "It is."

The D.A. agreed and was familiar with the Allen Charge Jury Instruction. She decided to tell them about it when they come back out.

Mr. Ericson said, "Frankly Your Honor if they're saying they can't all reach a verdict on one of the charges, I'd request a mistrial."

Duh! He knew goodin well what they were saying!

The jury returned to the courtroom claiming they'd reached a verdict. I was scared to death. Something just didn't feel right! Well, it was time to face the music.

"The jury has reached a unanimous verdict." My heart dropped. The bailiff asked the clerk to read it! She complied.

"In the case of The State vs. Juwan Jackson, you have returned a unanimous verdict, finding The Defendant guilty of trafficking in cocaine by possession. "Was that your verdict?"

Mrs. Griffin stated, "Yes ma'am!"

I almost passed out.

"Let the record reflect that each juror has indicated by their heads or verbally saying yes, that this is their verdict."

Judge Eve asked both attorneys whether they had anything further for the jury. They didn't.

The D.A. said, "The State is ready for the sentencing phase of this case! Mr. Jackson is a level one in this case. He pled guilty to a prior conviction in New York for disorderly conduct. Down here I believe disorderly conduct is a class 3 misdemeanor." The D.A. continued, "Your Honor, I'd ask that the bond be implemented, that Mr. Jackson be sentenced accordingly, Your Honor. Given the amount and the level of the offense, I will be asking that Your Honor, sentence the defendant Juwan Jackson to the $250,000 fine and consecutive sentences of 175 to 219 months."

Judge Eve asked my attorney for his stance on the matter.

He responded, "Thank you, Your Honor! Mr. Jackson is 42 years old. The information that I received from The State prior to this is that he had no criminal history, whatsoever! I asked him about the disorderly conduct, he doesn't recall that and at the most, it would be a misdemeanor. It's not a drug charge. This man has had business income in a company, Frozen Films. He is a taxpayer, he previously owned his own construction company. He's been involved in a film production company. I would tender to you that the trafficking by possession and the trafficking by transportation is really one in the same in this situation, it's about how the drugs got there. We disagree with the jury's determination but it's their verdict. But beyond that is to give this man a life sentence."

Judge Eve turned her nose up. She asked me if I had anything to say. "Yes Your Honor, but there's really not too much I can say at this point. I asked my attorney to put me on the stand several times and he refused to do so. I would've liked the jury to hear my side of the story. I gave up my right to be heard by sitting here saying nothing. At this moment I'm feeling like, you know, I guess I have to do what I have to do. Life is funny sometimes you know. Things happen for a reason, but in this case I really don't have too much to say"…

Judge Eve cut me off quick! "Well in the case of South Carolina v. Juwan Jackson, he has been found guilty of trafficking in cocaine. The court will sentence him pursuant to general statute, 90-95(h) (3), to a minimum of 175 to 219 months, both to run consecutively. He's in your Custody!"

I was escorted from the courtroom. My mind went blank. The look on Ericson's face was ice cold. I wanted to grab him and choke him out! I looked down, his fist was balled. I had paid him all his money. Why did he throw me to the wolves? Thirty-six years! "My life is over!" Where was all my so-called friends? How about Gloria and her bag of tricks? I guess that's the way the cookie crumbles! If I had it to do all over again, I surely would not have listened to Karen, her aunt Gloria and definitely, not Ericson! My life is over! That's the way the cookie crumbled!

Chapter 14

The Verdict

When I heard the verdict every one of my organs felt like the foreperson had said not guilty. Although, subconsciously, I never heard the word "NOT!" I looked over at Mr. Ericson. He had a look of total frustration and his stare was ominous. He knew what I was thinking. Yes, he had dropped the ball several times during the trial. Right now I wanted to knock his lights out.

An attractive young female bailiff walked up behind me and softly asked me to place my hands behind my back. I looked over her beautiful mane of hair and noticed my gay friend, Mike Nolan. He looked befuddled and afraid. While being cuffed, I yelled for him to take my rental car back to the airport. I had already given him the keys just in case something like this happened. He was standing there shaking his head in disbelief.

I felt as if they were parading me in front of the entire courtroom. I thought, "I will see each and every one of you again." My loss of control over my life freaked me out.

As the bailiff escorted me to the holding cell, there was a reflector as good as any mirror. I stood there and took a long look at myself. My tailored suit and alligator shoes meant nothing now. So for the last time I straightened up my tie and smoothed out my lapel. The female bailiff stood there with a sad look on her face as if we were old acquaintances. She warmly asked, "Baby why didn't you take the plea?"

I glanced at her and then back into the reflector and replied, "Because I am not guilty! When I look in the mirror at myself, I see a man, not a rat!"

She must have overheard me talking to Mr. Blue and Rick buster when they offered me probation not to go to trial. My attorney told me I had made the right choice earlier.

A few seconds after she made that statement, 3 male sheriffs entered the room. "All right Ms. Perez, we got 'em now! We'll take it from here."

After she left one of the 3 men said, "Boy how I'd like to hit those skins!"

The other 2 agreed and laughed. One of them said, "Okay big fella it's time to get you outta here. Yeah, it's time to transport The State's property!"

I don't know why those statements didn't seem to bother me and I wasn't in panic mode, but everything was happening in slow motion again.

They escorted me to another part of the building through an underground tunnel. There, a short fat officer with a raspy deep voice yelled out, "Okay. Next!" Ten other men were standing in line in front of me waiting to be sized up by eye and given an orange jumpsuit. I remembered my size from last year when I had been arrested. When it was my turn to receive the jumpsuit, the harsh voice of the chubby sheriff made the hairs on the back of my neck stand up. I was not going to be able to do it! I looked at him and said, "Large! Everything large!"

He gave me a medium and hollered, "Next!" I picked it up and walked behind the guy in front of me who was waiting to take a shower. There were 4 guys already in the shower. When one came out, one more would go in. I didn't see what all the commotion was about just to pick up an orange jumpsuit and take a shower.

By the time I made it to the dorm I was mentally exhausted. I wanted to lie down and rest for a little while. That wasn't an option with 40 or 50 other men playing cards, talking on the telephone and being as loud as humanly possible. Nobody was sleeping. My idea went out the window.

I saw 5 telephones and decided to make my move for one of them. Each phone had several guys waiting to use them. I was too tired to get into a fight over a phone call anyway so I walked around. Besides, I didn't want to talk to anybody.

My thoughts traveled at a high velocity. How was I going to coexist in an environment like this? I was clearly at a disadvantage, never having been incarcerated before.

This was obscene. I had to listen to people that were half my age telling me what to do all day. That really broke me. I had to be taught how to move on the inside.

I knew there were rules - lots of them. Officer and inmate rules. I knew I had to learn on my own through trial and error. Nobody was going to have their way with me. I'd die first. That went for inmates and officers.

I knew I had no wins with my hands against the officers, but showing no fear is vital in a place like this. Information traveled from the county jail to the prisons and vice versa.

It was imperative that I let my mother know for sure that I was okay. Mike would call her and others to tell them about my situation. But she needed to hear it from me. I waited for the next guy to hang up. I walked swiftly over and grabbed the receiver. Nobody approached me. They just whispered and glanced in my direction.

My mother is a very strong woman. She had previously been running back and forth to court with another one of my little brothers. Bryan was arrested 12 years ago for murder. He and his teenage friend, Al Gangster, was the triggerman. In reality, he wouldn't bust a grape in a fruit fight. And in the end after Allen shot and killed the police officer, he tried to blame it all on my brother by yelling out in court, "Bryan gave me the gun! Bryan gave me the gun!"

Officer Jim was white and highly esteemed. Bryan at 16, unable to articulate his words, had the police form his statements in their own words, caused him to get a life sentence.

The conviction lacked essential elements to obtain a conviction, but nobody cared. Three young black boys charged and convicted of murder. Headlines read: "White Officer Murdered While Moonlighting!"

I called my mother's number first but got the answering machine. I didn't want to leave a message because the words wouldn't come out right. I dialed Mike and he answered on the first ring which made me think of Karen. He sounded stressed and asked me if I was alright. He told me to hold on while he grabbed a pen to take down any request I might have. Although Mike was gay, he was loyal and like having a little sister.

I told him to contact my mother and my brother Terence to let them know that I had blown trial. I asked Mike if he had returned the rental. I also asked him to give my keys and cell phone to my mother.

He didn't have much to say. I knew he was really upset. He kept quiet, long enough for me to detect his emotions. I told him to be safe and keep in touch! Then I hung up.

It was lockdown time. The jailor shouted, "Lockdown! Everybody! Lockdown NOW!"

People were scuffling around pulling out mats and putting up the games and cards. One of the officers said, "You! You're in single cell #2!"

It was the first cell on the bottom tier near the front entrance. It was empty. The door popped open and he watched closely as I walked inside.

There was a table with a connecting metal stool attached and cross from it a steel bunk with a very thin mattress about three feet off the floor.

I wonder why they had put me in that room. Everything worked on a first come first serve basis. The officers decided who got what cell. I started looking around for a hidden camera because I knew one had to be there. I strongly believed there was one.

I had to be cautious. I didn't want to give them any reason to think I was crazy and put me on medication.

I put my glasses down on the table and started to rethink my past. I decided to take a nap. I dozed off and a demon paid me a visit. My eyes were closed but my mind was playing tricks on me again. It seemed he was on my bunk, laughing at me, taunting and saying, "You're going to let those idiots win! You're going to let them get over on you like that? You know you're going to die in prison don't you? You're 42 years old. In 36 years you'll be a 78-year-old bedwetter. You won't be able to get an erection and your friends and family will either be dead or have long forgotten about you." He continued to say, "I can tell you how to beat them all! Pick up those glasses! Break them! Use them as a knife to pierce your neck. By morning you'll be dead!"

I remembered picking up the glasses and wrapping the glass part up in some toilet tissue before laying back down. All of a sudden I heard another voice say "Juwan! What are you doing? I am here for you! I will never leave you!" I jumped up, threw my glasses on the floor and fell soundly asleep.

The next morning after breakfast, 10 female officers came bursting into the block hollering, "Shakedown, Shakedown! Everybody out of your cells now!"

I was stirring in slow motion, but I did get up to see who was giving the commands. Once one of the officers reached my cell, I was putting on the bottoms of my jumpsuit. She said, "Step out and put your hands up on the wall."

I obeyed and she began searching my cell. I watched her closely hoping that she had completed her search and was about to leave. She stopped short and pulled the roll of toilet tissue out of its holder on the sink and began to open it.

Chapter 15

The Big House

Being escorted from the dingy jail to the prison was one of the more helpless measures of my life. Once inside the van, I realized that this must be how a cadaver felt in one of those sliding doors at the morgue.

The driver's route took us through more rural parts of the country. I took in the beauty of each passing tree and blade of grass. Even though the driver appeared to be driving at 100 miles an hour, he slowed down and pulled past a sign reading, "Welcome to Kirkland."

The door slid open. I took in what materialized to be miles and miles of barbed wire. It was literally breathtaking.

As the gate opened, I could feel the heat of hopeless eyes watching my every step. Provocative comments were hurled my way from prisoners who were working out on the yard. Though I was in good shape, I felt scrawny compared to most of the muscular and chiseled frames that were now waiting for me to join their society.

Once inside, the officials humiliated me by forcing me to strip naked and search every cavity of my body and my belongings. When I was ordered to spread my cheeks, I told the officer that wasn't happening.

They observed my New York tone and an officer with tobacco stained teeth replied, "Boys we got us another one of 'dem' city slickers."

I thought to myself, "Where's the southern hospitality? How could such an out of shape hillbilly be in charge of anything?" This was a nightmare of epic proportion. I wasn't even through the processing phase. How much worse was this going to get? Another officer whom I hadn't noticed until now was scanning through my file. Whatever he saw made him comment that I must have really pissed off the judge or somebody. He said that he had rarely seen a man get 36 years for the charges I was accused of. I smiled for the first time in weeks and said, "That's kind of crazy huh!" The hillbilly laughed in agreement with our conversation.

I was asked what size clothes I wore. The hillbilly sergeant told the guy with the file to get me 36-40 pants, a 3X T-shirt and large boxers. The clothes looked like 200 different people had worn them. They were dingy and smelled funny. I couldn't make out that smell. I swallowed my pride and kept quiet. I decided that my best course of action was to do and look like everyone else.

The sergeant said, "As a favor to The State of New York, I'm gonna put you in a single cell instead of regular population. It is in the mental health ward with a bunch of paranoid schizophrenics." I thought about Karen!

The other officers found all of this comical but was given a disappointing glare.

Deciding to try and find a rhythm to their system, I picked up my bag and waited for one of them to lead the way to my cell.

The younger officer led me down a dreary well-lit hallway with a door and an elevator at the end. A sense of doom set in, but I kept my chin up.

As we were on our way to the 4th floor, I couldn't help but think about my last few decisions. Had listening to my conscience or demon when I broke my glasses led to me being put into mental health? I wasn't crazy or irrational. I just had a weak moment from all the stress I've been under.

I watched the officer continue to flip through my medical record jacket. They may have found the broken glass in my cell which could be the reason I'm headed to the 4th floor.

The elevator doors opened. I was astonished. It was extremely loud. It sounded as if 30 people were using bullhorns. I couldn't decipher one word to the next. I just knew this was complete chaos and I wondered what I had gotten myself into.

Finally, we were buzzed into a separate room by a guy who looked like he could easily be a patient. The officer handed him my medical papers and he quickly turned to the back page.

He warmly said, "Hello Mr. Jackson." His tone was creepy. "How are you today?" I responded, "Guess it could always be worse." He smiled and told the officer he would take it from here. The officer looked at me and said, "Don't give anyone a hard time and you'll be in regular population in a few days."

I nodded. He disappeared. I was put into cell #9.

There were 10 mental health cells on the eastside and another 10 on the west. I wasn't allowed to have anything in my cell, not even an extra change of clothes.

I did have a box of roll-up cigarettes and a book of matches, which an officer had slipped me downstairs. He must have thought I was going to need a smoke. Although I didn't smoke, I rolled up a cigarette anyways. What the heck. I might as well start smoking because my life has already been taken.

I choked on the toxic smoke for the first few cigarettes. Eventually, I became used to the dizziness and nausea from smoking the strong tobacco.

After a while, my cell reeked of smoke. The other mental health inmates were making things in the cell block heat up. Of course they wanted to smoke so they started shouting out my cell number saying things like,

"Yo #9. Let me get a smoke. I'll get you back later."

All of this brought the officers to my cell. He opened my door and took a deep breath and frowned saying, "We can do this the easy way or the hard way." Not wanting to fight with him,

I reached inside my pillow and handed him a box of tobacco and a few matches. He told me that if he smelled anymore smoke that he would take all my linen and my clothes. That threat didn't scare me at all. I had more cigarettes already rolled under my mattress. After lunch, I lit another and blew it out a small hole. No one from my previous life thought I smoked because of how health conscious I am.

I thought about the coward-of-a-man, Jack Taylor. He had taken no responsibility for any of his actions and set me up to take a fall that ruined my career and my future. I contemplated how to get out of this situation. Could a little money help me out of this mess? I thought about my ex-girlfriends, about Gloria. My mind was racing. I was caught up in a whirlwind. The 4 walls of my cell were closing in on me.

How had I come from making plans to visit the Capital of West Africa and Senegal to film and participate in the political movement to overthrow President Abdoulaye Waters, to be in prison in a mental health ward? I felt sick to my stomach. My life had turned upside down. This was the end of my dreams and the beginning of a nightmare.

After 7 nights of mind-boggling thoughts, a correctional officer informed me that I was moving into regular population. All I had to grab was my t-shirt. He said to hold on a minute, he'd be right back. I paced the floor impatiently. I couldn't wait to get a smoke. After about 30 minutes the officer returned. He led me down a hall and into a pale room with a large cage inside. A prisoner sat there wearing a crimson jumpsuit. He had a fresh haircut and shave. He wore designer glasses similar to the ones I had. The officer told me to wait and someone would bring me a lunch tray.

I sat down, starving. I said, "What's up man? What do I have to do to get one of those fresh jumpsuits?"

He gave me the most envious look and said, "You don't ever want one of these! This jumpsuit means death! New Jack!"

I could tell from the way he said "Death!" He was serious!

With empathy, I apologized. He asked me how much time did they give me? I replied, "36 years!" He then asked me my crime. I said, "Trafficking Cocaine."

Then I got a surprise. Right in that cage I was being enlightened. He wanted to know if my attorney had filed an appeal in open court. I said, "No! I don't think so."

He then asked when did I blow trial. I told him 9 days ago. He said I had 5 days to file a written notice of appeal or waive my right to a direct appeal.

He told me to move quickly and not to sit in here procrastinating. He further advised me to find out who had the law books to start studying and file a one-page notice of an appeal from the sentence, immediately. Hesitantly, I asked him his name. He strongly said, "Robert Bacon!"

Robert told me he was on death row for killing a man over his wife and that he would kill him again if it were possible.

He had 3 lunch trays and offered me one. I was afraid at first.

He insisted. They consisted of tuna, fried potatoes and fruit cocktail. That was perfect since I hadn't eaten in a week. I was beyond hungry.

As I ate he continued telling me things he thought I should know. I learned a lot in the 20 minutes that I spent with him before an angry officer demanded me to follow him. He took me to G-17, my new assigned cell. It appeared larger than the mental health cell.

I asked an inmate were I could get some cleaning supplies. He pointed me to a guy who said he was the dorm janitor. Spud said he cleaned rooms for $2.00. My cell was filthy. I told him to go ahead.

He pointed me to a guy that sold cigarettes on credit. Then to another guy who had law books. I asked Spud if he could put me and the guy with the law books together. That wasn't a problem! Everything in here had a price. Postal stamps are money. Whoever had the most stamps controlled the yard.

A society of its own! From where I stood, it seemed like a long road to nowhere!

Chapter 16

Correspondence

On September 27, 2003, I was still in shock about how my life was in complete bedlam. In Kirkland Prison for 9 days and I had witnessed dozens of people outside the prison fences protesting against something that was short of a legalized execution. I was snapped out of my sullen daydream when one of the correctional officers started yelling "Mail call!" I listened for a minute and as I was about to walk away he called out my cell number. "Seventeen, you got mail!"

I was excited to see that it was from Jamille's mom, Debbie.

The letter was brief and to the point letting me know I had support, asking if I needed anything and informing me to hurry up and put them both on my visitation list. She ended the letter telling me that Jamille sent her love. "Yes!"

It really felt good to hear all that. Right after dinner I would respond to the letter. Jamille had her mom coming to see me. Darn! Jamille always surprised me. She would constantly do the unexpected. I missed my clever girl. Especially her obsession with shopping. She would spend her last on clothes and shoes and worry about the rent later.

Debbie thought her daughter was playing with my emotions and that I would hurt her. She was probably right, but Jamille always stayed a step ahead. She was one of the smarter ones.

After responding to Debbie's letter, I fell sound asleep.

At about 4:30 a.m. my cell door burst open and an officer tossed in 3 small bags and demanded that I pack up. I was shipping out. I thought to myself this can't be happening. I just got here.

I haven't had a chance to talk to a jailhouse lawyer so he could help me file my timely notice of an appeal.

According to death row inmate Robert Bacon, I needed to get this done within 14 days after being sentenced.

Transfer Intent

We arrived at the South Carolina Correctional Institution located on Broad River Road late in the afternoon. We passed several prison camps along the way and there appeared to be several more on the same road directly in front of us. Some weird person had come up with that idea. If you put all of those prisons together they would consist of numerous miles of fence and razor wire. I couldn't help thinking that somehow I was getting lost in the system. I hadn't even been fully processed and received my prison identification number. Nobody could find me without it.

My oldest daughter was about to give birth. I knew she would call every prison in South Carolina trying to find me to give me the news.

I was assigned to E-211. On my way there, I felt a strange tension coming from the many eyes that were on me.

A man who looked as if he was at least 65, was on his knees at his locker. I thought he was praying. When he saw me he said, "Yo man, I don't appreciate anybody trying to see what's inside my locker!"

I checked my immediate surroundings to see who was watching the scene unfold. Several men were watching intently. They seemed anxious to hear my response. I did the only thing that I knew how. I tackled the problem like a man. I told the old man, "First of all I wasn't looking in your broke old locker! And I don't have a problem kicking your feeble, decrepit behind if you don't watch your mouth!"

Everybody in the cellblock busted out laughing including the old man. This must have been a frequent setup for new guys because they all suddenly looked as if they were going to rip me apart if I touched the old guy.

I had to make it known that I would stand my ground and defend myself against any man or situation.

At this point, I threw my stuff in the locker and walked outside.

As soon as I walked outside, I saw a guy I knew from the street. He was surprised to see me. I started telling him about my case. Ronnie asked a lot of questions. I had to cut him off and take charge. I only told him what I wanted him to know. He informed me about a guy named Virgil on the west yard who allegedly studied law.

The biggest problem was meeting him because he slept on the west yard. A big barbed wire fence and a 300-pound guard stood between us. Under ordinary circumstances I would have given up on a silly idea of consulting a layman of law, but I was desperate.

Time to file my legal papers was running out. I found out that the only chance to talk to Virgil was by attending church.

Virgil attended church regularly. I found out about a session that was going on tonight. I planned to go and ask around for him.

I needed a vague description of this Virgil. Then I'd see what happened. In the meantime, I had to see about getting an opus number and an identification card.

Scandalous Gossip

My friend Mike Nolan still had my cell phone. He was contacting everybody's name that he recognized. He called up big Fish, Ronda Davis, Jamille, Sharon Smalls, Cassandra, Marilyn, Keith Smith the gay hair stylist, Karen and Greg Slovis at the studio. He even called Carolyn in L.A. He also called Donna, Saundra and others.

Although I had only asked Mike to call one person my mom, he called everybody except her. There was a lot of collateral damage because of all the phone calls and no way to rectify it, but at the moment I could have cared less.

He basically said, "Hello this is Mike... with Frozen Films Productions. I am calling to inform you that my boss and friend, Juwan, is no longer with us. He was convicted Friday! He was sentenced to serve 36 years. I almost passed out girl! I am trying to locate his whereabouts but I can't find him. It's like he's lost in the system. I have Frozen Films' contact information and I am going to try and keep the company up and running. I know he would want that. I'm going to do everything in my power to see him through this. Yep! I am 99% sure he's innocent of those charges and was set up. You should have seen all the lies they all told."

I could only imagine their responses to my situation.

Bartering Agreement

That night I found my way to the church by following the Bible toting inmates.

I immediately began searching the room for a light complexioned 40-something-year-old man with short curly hair. I approached a man fitting the description and asked if he was Virgil? He seemed friendly enough after I introduced myself until I asked him if he did legal work. He gave me the coldest stare possible, then asked me where I'd gotten my information. Then he started acting really paranoid panning the room as if I had a secret camera somewhere. I thought he was going to frisk me. I couldn't believe he was acting like that and assured him that I wasn't sent to set him up by prison officials. I told him that I was new to the intricate dealings of the legal system and that I was running out of time. I told him I really need your help to file a timely notice of an appeal. I don't have a clue as to how to do this.

He told me that he would write a letter to the Columbia, South Carolina Superior Court, requesting all my legal papers and would do it all for free under one condition. He said show up here tomorrow looking to receive a blessing from God!

I said to myself that's it - that's all you want? Cool! I can do that. I vigorously thanked him in advance for agreeing to help. He was very understanding and kind. We sat down together and listened to the church choir as they sang "God Is So Good To Me!"

The following day I had an orientation session to learn the rules of the facility. Every prison had their own set of rules. Then I was called into my case manager's office. He gave me the choice of either working for 40¢ to a $1 a day or attending school. Since I was determined to learn as much as I could about the law I chose school.

A G.E.D. class had started the next day. The block I slept in was a road squad and kitchen block so I was going to get moved. I started packing my things. I decided to keep my sheets and blanket because luckily, I had been given a new set.

Going to church had an impact on most people's lives. I couldn't believe how so many fooled with God. I was determined not to be like that. My mother always told me that Jehovah knows your heart. It made sense to me. I just couldn't get into it. I heard many stories about guys who had kept their noses in law books and found ways to give The State back some of the years they were originally sentenced to serve. Virgil was my ace in the hole, the trick up my sleeve. If anybody was going to help me out of this muddle it was him. He was sharp and didn't trust anyone.

Chapter 17

Business Reorganization

Right in the middle of another one of my daydreams, I was brought back to reality by an officer shouting. "Mail call, listen up guys. D-2!" That was my new dorm and bed assignment. I had mail. I was excited and wondered who had written.

In the letter, Marilyn Johnson started by asking how I was doing. She claimed that she loved me and nothing or nobody could stop her from helping me or coming to visit. She said, "Even though I'm married, you're still my man. I'll never stop loving you. You will always have a place in my heart!"

Mike had called her. He told her that I had blown trial and got 36 years. She thought that I was sentenced under the old law and would be out in 8 to 12 years. How I wish that were the case. According to Mr. Bacon the death row inmate, I would do the minimum 28 years. She closed the letter with the imprint of her perfectly shaped lips and said, "I'll visit you by the end of the month." Yes! That was about 3 weeks away.

Here on the west yard, there seemed to be an abundance of jailhouse lawyers. It was like a lawyer's convention. My friend Virgil distrusted most of them with only negative things to say. He did communicate with this old white guy named Gary

Pittman, who actually looked and act like my idea of an attorney. Mr. Pittman was polite and very professional, but as soon as he heard my entire story he was galvanized into anger. Evidently, he hated judges and lawyers and decided we should bring a claim against them for their wrongdoings. Virgil warned me to watch out for Pittman's greed and to study the law for myself. Since this legal jargon was foreign to me, I hired Mr. Pittman's secretary or sort of paralegal, Charles.

Charles was a huge man tipping the scales at 300 plus with massive shoulders and a bulky but not out of place tummy. Charles worked closely with Mr. Pittman. He sported a neatly shaved head, pencil line for a beard and he was the darkest black man I had ever come across. He picked up and dropped off Mr. Pittman's papers with the swagger of a real professional. I was told by both Charles and Mr. Pittman not to worry about anything because I would win in appellate court and would be going home soon. I had organized a legal team. I was studying and reading every piece of law concerning my case that I could get my hands on.

Mr. Pittman had rewritten my notice of appeal. I dealt with him and Charles because eventually, everyone consulted with them anyway.

Guys who did legal work would come for advice and finishing touches on their briefs and petitions. Pittman would have them running back and forth to the canteen like rabbits. Mr. Pittman smoked like a chimney and he never ran out of cigarettes. He'd be rolling and smoking at the same time. His breath smelled like Ox!

I couldn't see how the men that sung on the choir could stand it. Thinking about it made my belly ache. Mr. Pittman and Virgil both sang on the choir. Virgil always stood on the opposite side. He had been victimized a few times before.

Clerical Correspondence

I was in class when I heard my name called over the PA system to report to the mailroom. My teacher, Ms. Jones, excused me to go directly to the mailroom and straight back. Several inmates had already lined up to pick up their legal mail. I simply followed what everyone else was doing. I heard the other guys calling the man in the white shirt Lieutenant Miller. When I reached the window I said, "Hi Mr. Miller."

He asked me for my identification card. I didn't have one. I told him that and he asked me my name and bed assignment and passed me the envelope. As I turned to walk away he said, "Hold up!" Demanding that I open the envelope in front of him.

As I responded to his semi-aggressive request, I decided to try my luck and inquire about where I could check my emails and send a fax right away. Suddenly I heard laughter all around me. Lieutenant Miller had a hysterical look on his face.

"Do you realize where you are Mr. Jackson?"

I hadn't really thought about that.

"You cannot run your business affairs from in here! Nor can you send any e-mails, faxes or text messages. And you surely can't receive any! Is that clear Mr. Jackson?"

I walked ed away feeling hopeless. How was I going to run Frozen, and provide for my children?

My letter was from the South Carolina Superior Court clerk Mary Lewis. She informed me that she had acknowledged my request for all the legal documents regarding my case. The papers were enclosed. Any further action had to be submitted in the form of a Motion for Appropriate Relief. This letter did not refer to any part of my notice for an appeal.

I sat down with Mr. Pittman. We went over my 2 indictments and my judgment and commitment papers. Pittman kind of sighed while shaking his head exclaiming that they couldn't do this. "Can't do what," I asked?

He ranted off 2 things. "One, both indictments have the same charges and statute numbers. That's double jeopardy. Two, the indictments state that you are charged with a Class H, which is a misdemeanor!"

Mr. Pittman was pissed when his assumption had been correct and no response to the notice of appeal. He seemed to know what The State would do in most cases before they did it.

We began putting our ducks in a row to file a motion for appropriate relief. He asked me if I knew anyone who would write an affidavit for me.

Savior

I walked to the front of the church looking for Virgil.

He always sat in the front row along with Mr. Pittman. I looked all over and couldn't find either of my friends. I waited until I heard the announcement through the PA system saying that church call was complete. This meant that no one else could leave the dorms to come to church. Not wanting to be here without neither of my friends, I stood up and headed towards the exit. That's when it happened. A tall Indian looking man started speaking into the microphone at the front of the church. He said, "You can leave now and miss your blessings or you can stay and receive them. The choice is yours!"

I looked around and saw that he was talking directly to me.

He said, "The message I bring here tonight is from the Lord!"

I laughed inside but could hear my mother saying "Boy you better run from them...demons!"

The preacher continued, "He knows all about the lavish playboy lifestyle you were living with all those different women. He gave you everything you needed to get the job done, but you still wanted to do things your own way." I was frozen!

"It's gotta be the F.E.D.s. Nobody else in here could have known all that! I'm outta here!"

I became paranoid because I hadn't even told Virgil or Pittman about any of that.

Did this man have mystical powers to contact God? I wanted to confront him about where he had obtained his information and tell him to mind his business. Yeah! I turned in his direction and began to approach him. The closer I got, the funnier I felt.

All of a sudden my legs buckled and I fell to my knees. I was scared, angry and embarrassed. I literally crawled the remaining few feet to the Indian preacher. He was standing tall!

He stared at me with a devilish grin with his arms stretched out wide. Once I reached his feet, he put his hands on my head and said repeat after me! I was so emotional that I wanted to cry out to my mother and I remembered her telling me when I was a kid and had bad dreams to call out to Jehovah! I felt pressured.

The preacher was talking and I couldn't understand a word he was saying. It was like an out of body experience.

I felt a strong, deep hold on me. I couldn't move. I burst into tears! I couldn't contain or control these tears and emotions. I hollered out, "Jehovah!" The man lets me go. I cried as I was being helped up. I thought I was hallucinating because as I lifted my head, I saw Virgil standing there with his hand on my shoulder crying also. I remembered the last time I cried like this, it was at my father's funeral. My grandmother held my hand.

Unequivocalness

The first night after I had my demonic experience, I had awakened at 3 a.m. in the morning. I didn't have an urgent need

152

to use the bathroom but decided to go anyway. I scanned the dormitory. It seemed that everyone was asleep. Even the officers who were paid to stay alert had fallen into slumber.

I was seeing things with a new set of eyes as I noticed the uncovered faces of a lot of the inmates. So many of the "convicted" killers, drug dealers, addicts, rapists and even child molesters appeared content, almost happy and satisfied to be here.

During the day time everyone seems to be busy. The majority of guys either work unit jobs such as the kitchen, clothes house or cleaning up the dormitories.

Others take up the various classes offered. Those that don't fit into either of these categories with idle time on their hands appear busier than anyone. They entertain themselves with a host of different activities.

Inmates gambled, played cards, watched television or got high on K-2 and bop to the music on their radios.

You have a group of guys who spend every minute trying to masturbate while staring at a female officer from a distance, usually in the bathroom. You also have those who do the same thing watching other men.

Then you have the self-contained hustlers who sell everything they get their hands on. Photos of fully naked or half-naked women.

Finally, you have the artistic bunch. These guys are truly talented. They can draw or do tattoos, and make useful objects out of anything from empty potato chip bags, sheets, old boots, shoestrings, toothpicks and popsicle sticks. Jewelry boxes, watchbands and picture frames are just a few items these creative guys can make. Homemade knives called "Shanks" originated from anything from a nail to a chicken bone.

They even make wine and liquor we call "Buck." Being in here, which is what we refer to as "the belly of the beast," is like being in an alternate world. Just when you thought you'd seen or heard it all, someone would do or say something you've never seen or heard of before. One thing is for certain, you can be anybody you want to be and life inside is unpredictable.

Chapter 18

Post-Conviction Matters

I sat at the table my mind fixed on learning what the statutes really meant. The terms were a bit confusing. Some of the words were even written in Spanish. It was hard to understand. The phrase "Darnum, absque, injuria," it meant damage without a wrong. How so, I thought? According to this red book, there is no cause of action without a wrong. I had learned the letter of the law or according to this, the spirit of the law. Mr. Pittman showed me some things but I mostly learned on my own.

Since I was not in a position to hire Johnny Cochran or any southern attorney that could get me out, I had to do this myself.

I was devoted.

Mr. Pittman appreciated my new enthusiasm as we began drafting my motion for appropriate relief.

I called my friend Mike to ask if he remembered the conversation on the first day of trial when my attorney, Mr. Ericson, told us about Judge Eve's friendship with my ex-girl Sharon?

Mike did remember. I asked him if he would write a sworn affidavit about it and send it to me right away. He agreed to do it expeditiously.

When I told Mr. Pittman about our conversation, he made sure that I knew Mike was my only friend and would be the reason for my early release.

Virgil was what we call a short-timer. He had gotten released a month before I filed my Motion for Relief.

Since we had become good friends, he promised to keep in touch. That was the first time I had heard that promise. After listening to the old timers talk they said, "It doesn't ever happen."

Mr. Pittman told me that my motion would likely be denied at the county level. He said, "We'll file a petition for a Writ of Certiorari!" - another Spanish term. I had an onslaught of questions for Mr. Pittman. I'm sure the poor man was getting weary.

I became a sponge, soaking up everything pertaining to law.

I listened and searched with an eager purpose. I turned to page 71. It said that "Certiorari" was a Latin word meaning: a writ issued by a higher court to a lower court requiring the certification of the record in a particular case so that the higher court can review the record and correct any actions taken in the case, which are not in accordance with the law.

That made perfect sense. Because why would the court that convicted me want to admit to any wrongdoings?

I thought about my friends. I wanted badly to believe that I could count on them when I really needed them. I learned what friends really meant after my incarceration. Everyone has a personal and financial agenda for associating with people. Mr. Pittman told me that everyone in my former life was useless! Except for Mike. The harsh reality was that Pittman was right.

Reunited

Later that day, I received a pink slip informing me that I would have a visit the next day. I had no clue who was coming but was happy about it. As I walked into the visitation room, I did not know what to expect. I glanced around the room and I heard a familiar voice say, "darn." I could not believe my ears or my eyes. There stood my younger brother Terence at 6"4', 260 lbs., otherwise known as "Big Fish."

Everyone was watching us hug and embrace. We finally sat down and started talking. He told me about his attempt to contact my trial attorney to persuade him to appeal my case.

Someone had just recently shot at an attorney for misrepresentation and breach of contract.

Everyone was frightened of people they didn't know.

Mr. Ericson's secretary had told Terrence that he was in Superior Court when he asked for the lawyer's whereabouts. He was pointed towards a man in a dark blue suit.

When Big Fish approached him and asked if he was attorney John Ericson, Mr. Ericson looked frightened and said, "No!" and disappeared inside the courtroom. We both started laughing frantically. At the moment it felt just like old times.

Then we both just kind of stared at one another tacitly. I needed to get out of prison. I didn't belong here. What was my purpose for being here?

I could hear my mother's voice saying, "bad association spoils useful habits, Juwan!"

The guard said, "Visitation hours are over!" Fish stood up. He promised to visit as often as possible to keep the family together and update me on any major changes.

I was relieved to see my brother. Those 2 hours had flown by.

It wasn't enough time! I felt a pang in my heart.

He gave me my parting hug, patted me on the back and told me to stay strong and keep my head up. He turned, walked out with the other visitors and never looked back.

It was the first time in my life I truly felt alone. I wanted to go home! It was mentally and emotionally exhausting.

All I wanted to do was curl up in my bunk and cry, but I had to be strip searched first.

Negotiation Agreement

It seemed as if life was happening at record-breaking speed. I needed to figure out how to slow things down. This law learning stuff was getting expensive. I was going to have to find my niche in order to survive if I wanted to continue learning the law. Everything cost. The books were expensive. I had to pay someone to type the motions. Postage was a factor and Mr. Pittman and Charles needed cigarettes, cookies, and cakes.

I asked Mr. Pittman what was taking so long for the courts to answer. He simply replied, "Any day, we'll hear something, any day now. Just relax. You'll be home soon!"

Certificates Manipulation

Mary Lewis the head court clerk, was making sure Susan was a team player. According to Denise's evaluation, Mary knew that Susan was working out just fine. Mary walked in the room to see Susan staring at a typed document with a puzzled look on her face. Mary asked to see it.

It was Juwan Jackson v. The State of South Carolina. It had been received March 23, 2004. A judge needed to see it right away. Mary asked Susan if any other exhibits accompanied the document and Susan mentioned the sworn affidavit. Mary told Susan to detach the affidavit and docket the motion to be heard today. Susan was confused. One minute she was supposed to use the stamp with the judge's name on it and the next, docket them to be heard.

Susan had been separating Pro se motions from their exhibits for over 6 months and was still unclear as to why she was supposed to do that. Internally, she acknowledged how unfair these practices are to all pro-se litigants pursuant to State Statute 15A-1420(b) (1).

A judge had to deny a motion or petition if it lacked the documents to substantiate the facts and or allegations presented in the motion. Susan wondered if the judges knew that the clerks were keeping them in the dark by removing the exhibits and leaving them no other recourse but to deny the motion.

She really cared about other people. Mary could care less. She had stock invested in the prison system.

Legal Objective By Criminal Means

Mary received an urgent phone call from Mr. Ericson complaining that a clerk had slipped up. He couldn't understand how Jackson's case had made its way to the court of appeals docket. "How in the world would a judge rule for that case to be heard?"

She was furious because she had just recently checked up on Susan. Everything seemed to be working out fine. Susan was doing her job exactly as she had been instructed. Had Susan intentionally disobeyed or was this an accident? There was no way to tell but something had to be done.

Mary called a meeting. She picked up the phone and yelled, "Denise! I need to see you in my office, now!"

Denise rushed right in but didn't have an answer to what happened in Juwan Jackson's case.

The only thing to do now was to call in a favor at the appellate court clerk's office. She knew and worked with clerks from all the courts. Years of lunches, dinners and retirement parties, plus some useful leverage from learning all the dirty little secrets revealed at the many Christmas parties she attended every year. She knew exactly who to contact to get Juwan's mysterious appellate relief sabotaged.

Clearly, inmates were her investment and time was on her side. Years of service without even a blemish on her record. She was determined to keep it that way! Somebody would take the fall, but it surely wouldn't be Mary!

Part 2

"Who's, In Fact, Causing Justice To Be Blind"

Chapter 19

Infradig Business

It was another one of those squirmy mornings. On Saturday, around 6:30 a.m., I was given a pink visitation slip for another visit. The female officer who handed it to me acted as if she resented handing me anything. She looked as if she didn't think I deserved a visit.

It was a warm gorgeous day. Since I had no clue as to who was coming to see me, I scurried about to get a nice shave to look sharp for the visit. I didn't want anyone to see me looking like a total fiasco. My messy hair needed maintenance.

I eased into the visitation room hoping to get a glimpse of my visitor before being spotted. I noticed Marilyn right away. She was clearly the best-looking woman in the entire room, stunning with her quarter cut Luis Vuitton boots, the color of her Gucci dress. The most memorable thing about her outfit was the 18 karat gold diamond pendant which I had given her as a gift in 1996.

Marilyn always had a lovely smile. I realized that I was smiling brightly also. We hugged each other tightly. I closed my eyes. There was a brief reminiscence of the love we once shared.

In a concerned tone, Marilyn paused and said, "I can't believe you're in prison! What you need me to do! Tell me, I'll do anything!"

I explained to her that I needed her secretarial skills to type up a motion I was working on. She agreed. We spent the rest of the 2 hours catching up. She promised to always stand by my side.

I let her do most of the talking. I loved her country accent.

I knew I would prohibit her from ever visiting me again.

I refused to be dissuaded from learning the law by any woman from my past. I couldn't fully delve into my case with outside distractions. I appreciated Marilyn's loyalty. It touched my heart. When the guard made the announcement that it was time to leave, I felt relieved. Marilyn held her departing hug longer than anyone. I could feel the guard's impatience so I whispered in her ear, "You have to leave now."

In my heart I knew that I needed this woman, but I decided that it would be easier on both of us if I cut ties after getting my motion typed up. She was married. I didn't want to come between that any more than I had already.

Mysterious and Injudicious

I was shackled, put into the back of a transportation van, on my way back to the county jail. The appellate court had ordered the lower court to review the judgment of my conviction which meant reviewing the reasons for the 36-year conviction that I received on September 10, 2003.

Boy, I was happy. Pittman said this day would come. The writ we'd put together had finally paid off. I felt sensational.

Once at the courthouse, I was placed in a holding cell where I received a visit from an attractive young lady claiming to be my court-appointed attorney.

She had dark caramel colored skin and an athletic body dressed in a fitted but not tight olive colored pantsuit. Her hair was closely cropped above her ears with burgundy highlights and appeared to be in her mid-30s fresh off the bar exam.

She had an arrogant demeanor. She politely introduced herself, but there was something very distasteful about her. She carried a small file under her arm. I couldn't tell whether it was mine, but I sure hoped not!

I informed her that the attorney general had agreed with me on all the allegations in his response to my writ. He requested that I be granted an appeal and an evidentiary hearing.

The lawyer stared at me for a moment before shooting me down. Her face disappointing and angered. I had the attorney general's brief supporting my statement, but decided against producing it at this time. She told me she would see me in court and turned to walk away.

Ninety minutes later I was standing in front of a judge.

He sat there eyeing me as though I was dinner, a tempting dinner he couldn't wait to consume. I just hoped he could digest what I was prepared to do and say without hitting me with more time.

I felt closely watched as I organized my legal papers on the table in front of me. He looked as if he could decipher all the ligaments in my brain… if indeed I had any.

I put my papers in order and listened to the D.A. and my fine stuck-up attorney argue back and forth. I could hear Mr. Pittman's voice telling me to stay on my P's and Q's. And to make sure to object in open court if I suspected anything fishy, especially if it sounded like they were saying things that didn't apply to my case. After several minutes it happened.

I fiercely blurted out! "Objection Your Honor!"

The courtroom looked like a scene out of a movie with Jack Nicholson. Everyone froze. The judge stared at me with extreme zeal. He was waiting to hear the reason behind my objection since he had to rule on it. I held my head high and boldly stated, "Your Honor, I'd like for you to state for the record the nature of these proceedings."

Both my lawyer and the D.A. looked at me with disclaim, not believing that I made an objection. They could not imagine that I knew the importance of asking such a question.

Finally, the judge smiled acknowledging my attempt to interfere with the attorney and the D.A.'s incessant bickering, all of which was undermining my chance to obtain justice.

The judge calmly said, "Mr. Jackson, we are all here today to comply with the appellate court judge's order to determine your indigent status and to appoint you counsel on your appeal and to decide whether or not to grant you bond while your appeal is pending." He didn't insult my intellect by asking me if I understood what that meant. I thanked him and continued saying, "I didn't come prepared to argue the bond issue, but if it pleases the court, once that issue is addressed I have a document to present to the court to review."

I also stated that I have a document from the attorney general saying that I should have an evidentiary hearing on the issues brought out in my petition for a writ of certiorari.

The judge replied that he wanted to take a look at that document. I reached over the table and handed it to my attorney. She briefly examined it as I waved her to give it to the judge.

I didn't want to waste any of the courts time. She slowly walked up and handed it to the judge. He stared at the first page, immediately nodded affirmative and then stated,

"I see where you're going with this Mr. Jackson and I should set a date for an evidentiary hearing."

The D.A. turned apple red and said, "OBJECTION, Your Honor! The senior resident judge in this district has already denied Mr. Jackson's motion for appropriate relief. An evidentiary hearing was also included in his denial order. I don't think it would be proper for this court to go against an original order and grant him a hearing now!"

The judge's expression lets me know that no help would come from him on that point. He did ask my attorney for her stance on the matter. To my astonishment, she quickly stipulated with the D.A. that the matter had already been adjudicated.

That's when I objected. I had to speak then or forever hold my peace!

"Your Honor, I don't stipulate anything that The State has said or done here today or at any time as it relates to me and my case Your Honor. I'm sorry but I don't even know my court-appointed attorney's full name. If she wants to agree with the State that I shouldn't get a hearing on the constitutional issues raised in my petition, then she should go over there and standby the D.A. I pointed to the table where he stood. He was furious.

The judge banged his gavel and shouted, "Order in my courtroom! Order!"

When the tumult subsided you could hear a pin drop.

The judge continued by stating, "We are here to decide the bond topic and to appoint counsel. Mr. Jackson, let me see the document you mentioned earlier."

I handed it to my so-called legal representative. She went through the motions of scanning it as she frowned, then sauntered toward the judge and handed it to him.

He then nodded his head for the second time as if he was sorry before making a decision.

He finally spoke saying, "Mr. Jackson, I'm going to be honest with you. My boss has denied your motion, and bond was included so I can't grant you an appeal bond."

I said, "I understand Your Honor, but the higher court says those matters are to be reviewed. I'm mainly concerned with the attorney general's response that I receive an evidentiary hearing."

The D.A. stood up when he made his objection. "Apparently the Attorney General's Office agrees with Mr. Jackson, but my office does not! If the attorney general wants him to have an evidentiary hearing let him come down here and give him one, because my office do not agree!"

No one in the courtroom could believe what they had just heard. They froze again. After his words had sunk in you could tell he regretted his outburst.

I started rubbing my hands together as if molding a piece of clay into a ball. I wanted his statement to be easily found on the last page of my transcript.

The judge stared at me as if reading my mind before I spoke.

I replied, "Your Honor if we are finished here today can you please sign a judicial order sending me back to Kirkland."

He smiled and said, "I'm doing that right now Mr. Jackson. This court is adjourned!"

I couldn't wait to get back so I could brag to Mr. Pittman about how well I handled myself in court today.

When I left the courtroom, a lady sheriff said, "You think you're a lawyer. You ain't no lawyer!"

We both smiled at each other.

Chapter 20

Promissory Notes

I was becoming pessimistic at this stage of the game. Nothing seems to be going my way. I had to stay positive. Mr. Pittman quizzed me unexpectedly. As much as it angered me it really kept me sharp. Any time I would answer incorrectly he would make sarcastic remarks as if he had acquired all of his knowledge during the short amount of time that I had been studying law. He used to piss me off! I found it offensive for him to compare his extraordinary understanding of the law to my secondhand learning, but I knew he wanted the best for me so he pushes me to the limit. Coming into the system knowing little or nothing about anything regarding the law, I know I have come a long way.

I made written promises to pay those who were responsible for helping learn how to win in a legal battle. I now have the significant information needed to build a strong foundation. Pittman, calls in an affirmative defense. He drilled into in my head that without it you can't triumph over the other side. I didn't know all of my civil rights, but I knew most of them. I studied hard when it came down to issues involving my constitutional guarantee against discrimination by reasons of race origin, religion, gender, age, or disabilities, under the 13th,

14th and 15th amendments to the U.S. Constitution. I understand why a gentleman has to know the law of the land because he never knows when he will have to apply it to himself. My rights, my very self, would never be violated again.

I was advancing at learning the law and the officers could see it. I spoke up for others even faster than myself. I started helping other inmates with the legal problems. I was practicing law without a license. I had them sign a promissory note to pay me whether or not the results were favorable. I'd charge a retainer to even read their paperwork. I'd explain that their promise to pay a specific amount by a specified date was binding in a court of law.

I'd go to Mr. Pittman for help just like everyone else if it was something I did not understand. I managed to get a hold of a lawsuit prepared by a real attorney. I use his format and changed the statutes and case law to fit the situation. I had read so many cases that I knew which case was closest to the point of each individual that I worked with.

I give public notice to the court that I was about to bring an action against whoever the defendant was at the time. I also give personal notice to the person concerned. I studied the prior time during which a civil action may be brought after the injury occurred or became known.

My friend in New York taught me to always bring proof that speaks directly to the issue requiring no support from other evidence. Proof based solely upon a witness's own knowledge, as distinguished from evidence from which inference must be drawn if it is to have value as proof. In other words, only argue the things you can prove. That's how he won all his cases he would incessantly say.

Most inmates were happy to pay for any help that they would receive. The sad part about it is, that they wouldn't even bother to check to see if I was sighting the right statutes or not. If you ask them the name of the judge or district attorney's name in their case, they couldn't tell you. You'd think if a person gave you 5, 10, 15 years to do you'd try to know everything about them.

Six months of easy hustling had passed. Mr. Pittman's assistant, Charles, finally got caught. He didn't even see it coming. Sergeant Odem walked up on him while he was playing cards. He secured Charles with handcuffs and escorted him to his locker where the sergeant vigorously searched Charles' pockets, shoes and even made him open his mouth.

It was obvious that a jailhouse snitch had something to do with this. Sgt. Odem took Charles' key and opened his locker. After a brief show of searching, he then opened a 'One A Day' pill bottle and found over 100 Hydroxycut Pills. He then opened 2 roll-on deodorant bottles and found $500.00 in cash.

He continued his thorough search finding close to 2 ounces of marijuana inside a baby powder container.

It seemed strange that he knew to shake all the baby powder out, which exposed the marijuana. He knew exactly where to look. He made a big show of hauling Charles off to segregation.

There was no way to know how long Charles would be in the hole. Half the yard owed him or should I say, "owed us money." Since I was the person who funded the operation. I knew there would be plenty of messages coming my way about who owed what and of course I had to put Charles share away somewhere.

I was not looking forward to this part of our arrangement, but it had to be taken care of.

Charles had a cousin on the yard who started telling people to pay him on Charles' behalf. I learned of this after several guys came to me complaining about paying their bill twice. I could not blame them for not wanting to be in the middle of a very nasty collective bargaining arrangement.

Charles' cousin, Mike, had put me in a terrible situation by trying to interfere with my money. He was swimming in deep water with his treachery. I hope he knew how to swim among sharks without being eaten alive.

I walked outside to check on the canteen line where inmates would be lined up anxious to spend their family's hard money. Charles' cousin, Mike, stood towards the front of the line collecting a large trash bag full of goodies that belonged to me and Charles. He was collecting these items with authority as if he had legitimate rights to collect payment he didn't deserve.

I maintained my cool and recognized an inmate who owed $30.

I had a list made out for him in my pocket and gave it to Mike.

I needed a response to determine a course of action. I said, "Hey man, what's up?" He nodded without speaking which made me nervous. I stared at him and politely asked if he had a problem with the list?

Everyone knew Mike couldn't read, but he pretended by shifting his eyes from left to right. He was an expert at making people believe he could read. He then said, "Nah man, I don't have a problem with it."

I smiled and felt relieved as I handed the list to Green Eyes. Everything seemed alright, but I had an uneasy feeling that this was about to go wrong.

Several minutes later as Green Eyes moved closer to the canteen window, Mike said, "Yo, you know what Green Eyes, don't even worry about that list. It's dead. You don't owe either one of us."

Green Eyes nodded okay. I could feel my body temperature rise. I was sure steam was coming out of my head. This was territory I wanted to stay away from. I was losing my temper. I slowly approached Mike. He stood there like a lump on a log. I really needed this situation to be explained to me because I was mad and confused. I asked a very serious but ambiguous question, "So Mike, what you are really saying is forget me and my money!"

Mike licked his lips as he glanced around with a dumb smirk on his face. He said, "Nah man. I'm just canceling the debt. That's all."

My mind started racing. THAT'S ALL! What the heck did he mean! This dude has lost his mind. He has nothing invested.

He must be "cuckoo for Cocoa Puffs," but I'm going to show him crazy.

I asked Mike to take off his glasses and there was a sudden outburst of laughter. Mike didn't find my demand funny so he responded, "I'm not taking off...nothing!" But before he could finish his statement, BOOM! I hit him with a vicious right. His entire body staggered back against the wall, he wasn't moving. He was out on his feet. Everyone was in shock and awe. I too was amazed until Mike came out of it.

He went straight to the officers. Two minutes later they were calling me over the PA system. "Juwan Jackson, report to E-Dorm operations desk immediately!"

I instantly regretted my decision but I had to maintain some kind of respect. I knew what was coming. I was going to join Big Charles in segregation and that was not good.

At least people would know not to mess with me, my money, or my rights.

Chapter 21

The Choices We Make Determines the Life We Live

When I arrived at the north side of the facility, I thought everything appeared calm, everyone seemed relaxed. It was strange. Then it became obvious why things were so laid back. Most prisons have adopted a debit system where money is put on a card, which is usually also your identification. Not here. Inmates refer to this as a cash camp, where actual American currency is spent and passed from hand to hand. These guys were spending big face bills that looked like monopoly money. It had been 26 months since I had seen any dividends.

This camp looked like an old hospital. Extremes amount of re-painted surfaces. Asbestos everywhere. I didn't have time to give way to anxiety. I had to keep my head straight and get back to work. Shipping me away from Charles and Mr. Pittman was a melancholic situation. It was sad and miserable.

The superior court appointed me an attorney. From day one I didn't trust the guy. He had tricks for days. It would take at least another month before their rendered decisions on the briefs I had filed. It was imperative for me to find another jailhouse lawyer and law books. I didn't know if Mr. Pittman could be replaced.

I had to make my side of the facts known. I had a strong personal obligation because no one but myself was required to do those

36 years behind bars. My brief would be translated literally by the courts.

Two weeks passed. On the third week I was offered a canteen job. It was the sweetest job on the camp. It came with all kind of benefits. I could eat and drink up to $40 worth of merchandise without paying and not get fired and jailed.

If I took this job, a lot of money would touch my hands. It would be like old times!

My first thoughts were that this would be a calamitous disaster.

I knew that the devil would be close by watching, taunting, waiting to use his trickery and deceit.

I tried to decline this position, but the young lady who offered the job was very insistent. Her body language spelled trouble. The way she spoke to me was different. The way she said 'please' reminded me of my ex-girl Jamille.

When I tried to explain to her that I was working on my legal case, trying to get myself out of prison, it went in one ear and out the other. She wouldn't take no for an answer.

I knew she had a reason connected to this canteen job other than cash. She informed me that she would train me personally.

For the first 2 hours our fingers and shoulders were constantly touching. She smelled fantastic. It had been a long time since I was virtually alone with a woman. As I started to get the hang of it, she stared at me for a moment and softly said, "Thank you Juwan. I'll see you tomorrow."

At that moment, I realized that maybe we shared an attraction, but in my situation I couldn't be too sure.

The women who work in these places knew how to use their eyes and gestures to get what they wanted. They knew that there were mostly weak men in prison, lusting for any little chance to feel the warmth of a woman.

She opened the door to leave. All the inmates waiting in line complimented her on one thing or another. The few that didn't simply said something like, 'Get home safe, Ms. Brown.'

She swiftly walked away without a single response. That was her way of letting me know she only wanted me.

Once I got used to the inmates' slang for purchasing items, the rest was a piece of cake. I worked hard, kept the money right and ran a clean canteen.

Deny and Delay

Mary had directed Denise to stall his transcripts from reaching the appellate court! An email had requested the record for the 3rd time that week. This tactic usually caused appellate attorneys to rush trying to meet the deadline, but mostly resulted in a quick motion asking the judge for an extension of time to file his brief. Mary's explanation and as far as she was concerned always paid off. In many cases pages went missing. The procedural process is regularly abused.

A petitioner's due process was incessantly misused and violated in a technical sense.

The adjective laws dictating how rights are presented for interpretation and enforcement, as distinguished from a substantive law that creates legal rights are overlooked, then avoided and outright groundlessly handled.

Some believe that it's inadvertently done, which is foreseeable on the surface, but underneath, it reeks of fraud.

Two weeks later, I received a letter from my court-appointed appellate attorney, Mr. Rodney Collins. He sent me a copy of the State's brief. The trial transcript contained 222 pages, including information informing me that the record of appeal had been filed along with a 33-page brief that Mr. Pittman and I had thrown together.

After several thorough readings, I found the State's brief sadly insufficient, inflammatory and lacking any exhibits supporting their theories.

I had learned a lot about how The State argues cases from reading other inmates paperwork. The same format and unrelated statutes and authorities were used repetitiously.

The attorneys for The State knew that Pro-se litigators did not have any knowledge or access to the meaning of certain state codes and rules.

*   *

During count time I am allowed to stay inside the canteen until count clears. It usually takes about 35 to 40 minutes, depending on who's counting in the control booth.

Ms. Brown came into the canteen with a seductive smile and an ankle-length form-fitting skirt.

She had received my letter of resignation and she wanted to know if I really wanted to quit.

I didn't want to look her in the eyes. That's how she swindled me last time.

I continued stocking the shelves although her scent was driving me crazy. I walked to the back trying to put some space between us, but she would not leave. I began to get weaker by the second.

I heard a soft thump and knew something had hit the floor.

I came around the curve to see what it was and was speechless.

There on the floor was a gold Trojan Magnum condom.

As I bent down to retrieve it I heard Ms. Brown say, "Juwan please don't quit. I need you! There's no one else that cares about the canteen the way you do!"

For the first time ever I didn't know what to do in this situation.

All kind of thoughts ran through my mind.

Was this a trick or a test? I just stood there with my mouth open!

Chapter 22

Gluttonous Nature

The several weeks of practicing my canteen skills seemed like an eternity. I was not sure about exactly what was going on. I thought I'd had her dancing to the beat of my drum, but since I'd spent most of my time in the canteen I may have been dancing alone. I had totally rearranged the inventory inside so that if I closed the business window you couldn't see inside. I'd felt that my life was starting to make sense.

Why Ms. Brown risked her livelihood for someone like me was unbelievable. She had no idea who I was. Still, it was fascinating. She mostly communicated desire with her eyes and facial expressions.

It was also very clear that I had not learned my lesson about dealing with married women. Heck, married women were the best at everything. They knew what I needed.

During these past weeks, Ms. Brown spoiled me. She would cook my favorite meals at her home and then hand fed me at work. For my birthday in July, she brought me five half pints of Hennessy. Things were going great, but like anything else, there is a beginning and an end.

The end of my newfound comfort came at 6:30 a.m. on a Monday morning. I was sweeping the canteen and noticed 2 male officers nearby ready to jump me. I had a flashback of the day of my arrest.

It all started after an inmate overheard Ms. Brown and me talking about how much we both enjoyed lamb chops and yellow rice pilaf. Neither of us noticed the inmate standing close enough to hear.

Shortly after this conversation, the inmate's version hit inmate.com. This inside network of gossipers, haters, snitches and news carriers never ever get anything totally right.

By the time they carried the statement to the officers in charge, it sounded like a whole different story. They made it sound like Ms. Brown and I were married. For this fact alone, we were investigated, which meant I got a free trip to lockup.

The big brass at every prison has little snitches that feed them enough information so that they can investigate other inmates or staff. They kept a watch on Ms. Brown with a microscopic eye, but she was good to me so the investigation yielded nothing.

Of course, I lost my job and remained locked up in segregation for 120 days until I was transferred to another facility. It was sweet while it lasted.

When I arrived at the 'new' to me run down facility, I noticed at once that the building was air-conditioned. It was nice to finally be cool, but my priorities remained the same. I had to make contact with the inmates with law books, who were into doing law work.

After organizing my personal property, I sat down to write my appellate attorney to let him know I'd been shipped to another prison. I was also demanding a visit within 30 days.

Twenty-six days later, I received notice that he was waiting for me in a private room. I had to sign papers giving him permission to see me. After the paperwork was complete, I was taken to the room where Mr. Collins waited. He greeted me with a warm smile. He knew I was a pretty intelligent guy after reading my handwritten petitions and legal briefs. He tested my knowledge of the law through a series of questions and remarks.

He said, "I have determined that I made a wise decision by closing down my private practice and becoming an assistant appellate public defender."

At least he got that part right because I was going to sue him if he didn't represent me the way I asked him to.

Mr. Collins reviewed all 8 of the errors in my case. He explained why he only argued 2 assignments of error in his brief. He reasoned that it weakens the brief to argue all 8 errors, due to limitations on the number of pages one could use.

I was confident about the arguments that Mr. Pittman and I had put together, which Mr. Collins submitted along with his brief. He further explained the options in the event the court ruled against both of our arguments. He told me the court would render their decision any day now. He told me that the arguments that I used were very good arguments, but would most likely be denied for being untimely.

He packed up his green book of appellate law and criminal procedure 2005, shook my hand and swiftly made an exit.

I sat there for another 5 minutes. Boy! How slick he was for bringing a 2005 law book and facing it down just to see if I'd recognize it.

I bet he had a lot to talk about when he got back to the office and told his boss that we really had that book and I pointed it out to him without ever seeing the cover. Amazing! Mostly because it was still 2004. Robert Bacon told me that those white families made sure their kids received any books that they requested. He was right.

Chapter 23

Investigator Inversion

After several long weeks of diligently searching for Sharon, the private investigator I hired to find her was narrowing down his leads. He had already combed the icy streets of Illinois without much luck. His investigation had drawn him north to Connecticut. When we concurred on this in the beginning, I had no prominent reason to believe that Sharon had moved to Connecticut.

After reminiscing about our time together, I began to deduce this made perfect sense. Connecticut is not far from New York. It is clean, low-key and quiet in terms of crime. The kind of place that Sharon blended in smoothly as a bartender's best Sex on the Beach cocktail. She was skilled in many areas so finding a job would not be a problem.

At 9:20 a.m. on a breezy sunny afternoon, Mr. Hartness, the investigator, came face to face with his prey. He introduced himself and informed Sharon that I hired him to find her. Her eyes swollen with tears of joy as she begun jumping up and down exuberantly. She was so happy! She couldn't believe it. "He kept his word! He found me! Come in! Let me get you something to drink!"

She fixed Mr. Hartness some coffee and a cup of green tea for herself. She told him how she'd met Juwan and about some of their business endeavors. Mr. Hartness enjoyed Sharon's company and found it easy to talk to her. He wrapped up his investigation. Sharon offered to drive him to the airport but he insisted on taking a cab.

Mr. Hartness contacted my appellate attorney Mr. Collins and my mother to let them in on his findings. They both seemed grateful. My mother was not convinced. She believed that Sharon should have done more to keep her son out of prison.

She knew that it was Sharon's Cadillac Escalade the police found the cocaine in. My mother told me the news about the P.I. finding Sharon.

I knew that after an appellate judge read my lawyers brief and found out about Sharon and Judge Eve's friendship, he would have no choice but to throw the case out! I had to get a new trial! Yes! This would be a clear conflict of interest.

A WEEK LATER...

My court appointed attorney Mr. Collins informed me that for internal reasons he would no longer be able to represent me. All my ears heard was "I quit!" The letter consisted of an email copy that he had sent to my private investigator, basically telling him the same thing about our status. He also requested the

P.I. to forward any new information he received directly to me or any attorney representing me.

This was a definite monkey wrench. I was blindsided by this breaking news. I thought we were doing so well on my case. I actually realized that the trust and expectations you place on man usually bring disappointment. I guess that's why my father used to tell me not to be a follower.

After processing all that was happening I made several attempts to contact Mr. Hartness. My letters never received responses nor did the emails that my niece Chelsey sent him. Everything went unanswered. My gut told me that something scandalous was going on, but for the life of me I couldn't come up with anything feasible. Is this what Gloria meant when she said my paperwork was all messed up.

Weeks had passed and I still didn't have any communication with the P.I. My mother even tried to make contact and couldn't. Things were turning for the worse very quickly. Domino effect of mishaps. My court appointed appellate attorney dropped my case without a full explanation. The investigator is M.I.A. He didn't even turn over the vital information he got from Sharon. At this moment in my life, if it wasn't for bad luck I wouldn't have any at all.

I contacted the head public appellate defender, Mr. Davis.

I explained to him how Mr. Collins quit. I complained about him being ineffective.

Mr. Davis became very defensive and flippant that I was talking about a lawyer this way. He told me that if this P.I. of mine didn't turn over his findings in a reasonable amount of time, for me to file a complaint with the Private Protective Service Board. I believed my darn attorney should have retrieved the information I needed.

After 2 weeks of unanswered attempts to make contact with the investigator, I filed a complaint with the Private Protective Service Board. The P.P.S.B filed my complaint and appointed another investigator to conduct a further investigation on the information I hadn't received. The new P.I., a Ms. Conney, took over and told me she would visit me within a week or two. She told me I could call her if I thought of anything else.

About 10 days later Ms. Conney came to visit me. She was a plump and very pleasant middle-aged lady. In one smooth motion, she removed a folder from her briefcase and shook my hand simultaneously. She assured me that she was going to get to the bottom of my situation. She said she saw a lot of interesting scenarios and that the elements of conspiracy reeked throughout.

She had that right! She seemed like the nosy type that would pry into my case with a crowbar. This was also a time to pray a long prayer. I got down on my knees and bowed my head.

Chapter 24

Hypothesize Arguendo

When Susan overheard the umpteenth individual speaking of rumors concerning clerical mistakes, she became suspicious. She acknowledged her squeamish feelings.

She considered the numerous documents she had handled.

She also knew that if any crisis emerged from this particular office, Mary and Denise would quickly shift the blame to her. The federal connecting rule would allow exhibits and testimony from either to be introduced into evidence on the condition that relevance could be shown at a later date by connecting all the evidence. She was doomed now that she was aware of the connecting nature of the training she had received from Mary and Denise.

Knowing it would be them against her made her think about turning to alcohol. Instead, she dug into her purse to retrieve the phone number of her family attorney.

She had prayed for this job. Why was this happening?

She couldn't believe it! The Review Board at the Federal Administrative Offices of the court could punish her to the fullest extent of the law.

She became paranoid about losing everything that she had worked for. She stared at the lawyer's number and decided to call him on her lunch break. She has to get her head together.

The secretary informed her that Mr. Ripps was not in and transferred her to his voicemail. Her brief message:

"Hi Mr. Ripps. This is Susan Porter and I may need to retain your services. As you may already know I am a superior court clerk. I would appreciate it if you would give me a call back at around 6:15 p.m. at home, please. My number is 803-735-9399. I will give you all the details then. Thank you in advance for returning my call."

Afterwards, she wondered if she should have said more but didn't dwell on the thought. She decided to visit the court's law library and do a little research of her own. Investigating was an area where Susan was very sharp. She looked up laws relating to the clerkship, clerical responsibilities, clerical error and civil liability. Then she went further with civil procedure and rules of procedures by which private rights are enforced by both Federal and State standards. She also checked on the elements of conspiracy, where she felt sure she was involved in a criminal conspiracy. Susan strongly needed legal advice.

Extraneous

Attorney Howard Ripps had worked for the Porters well over 20 years covering all their legal issues from tax to wills, inheritance and traffic tickets.

He waited until a little after 7 p.m. to return Susan's call to be sure she'd had time to get home and unwind a bit. Unlike most of his clients, he actually respected Susan's father, whom he played many rounds of golf with and considered a close personal friend.

While pouring a cup of tea Susan's phone began to ring. She wanted to ignore it but figured it would be the attorney. Not realizing she was staring at the phone, she finally answered on the 8th ring. Trying to sound out of breath, she picked up and said hello.

Mr. Ripps asked if this was a bad time. She said no and thanked him for calling. He began by telling her he would not bill her until he was sure that he could help, then got her comfortable with him by asking about the family, then asked her what his firm could do for her.

She was quiet for a brief moment and stated that she had a few legal questions she needed answered. He told her to continue. She said, "Hypothetically speaking, could a person go to jail if they knowingly, inadvertently or helped to change the outcome of a legal matter in a pending case?"

Mr. Ripps paused before responding which scared Susan. Then he told her no, but only if these actions were done with malice and spiraled over into criminal territory.

He then waited for her to continue with the rest of her paranoid schizophrenic scenario to see if she were hypothetically speaking or about something she was involved in. He then asked her what happened at work to make her believe she needed his assistance. Susan had been so flustered since these rumors had started that she had to tell somebody so she blurted out "Pro Tunc Filings! I've been instructed to detach the exhibits from the pro-se briefs and I've been separating the pro-se filings from the ones filed by attorneys. I have also been using a rubber stamp to sign Judge Myer's name."

Mr. Ripps thought the worse because he knew it was fraudulent to do that, but he answered, "Where's the harm in that? It sounds like you're doing exactly what I used to do 30 years ago. I was a student interning for the same superior court. I worked under Judge Myers in the Pro Se Department when he was a superior court judge. It was his first year and he used to have me doing all his work. I kept the stamp in my jacket side pocket."

He told her that he wouldn't charge her for the call and if anything else developed to be sure to contact him right away. Susan thanked him and said, "Goodbye."

Her research notes revealed to Susan that "Nunc Pro Tunc" was a Latin term meaning, now for then! It gave an act the same effect 'now', as it would have had 'then'.

Detaching exhibits from pro se documents strips the brief of its merit, giving the court jurisdiction to deny it.

Susan now wished she could undo her actions. She had committed fraud by altering documents. She knew that backdating the pro se papers had to be illegal.

Part 3

The Root of All Evil…

Chapter 25

Million Dollar Enterprise

While wondering what information Ms. Conney possessed about Steven Hartness's disappearance. I decided that the simplest approach would be to just ask her. I studied her countenance with pinpoint precision. She swallowed hard and then in a super low secretive voice, told me that he had been arrested. I was really disturbed by this small piece of information. I knew there was more. Every part of my being needed to learn everything so I asked her what had happened. She took a long deep breath to collect her thoughts and began her history of events.

She informed me that Mr. Hartness had been a former police officer in Greensboro, North Carolina. After retiring, he and his wife moved to Columbia, South Carolina to start a private investigation company. Shortly after taking your case he received another assignment which involved investigating police officers. Still a cop at heart, he knew the controversial nature and danger of investigating police officers from the Columbia S.L.E.D. Department.

He was hired by the District Attorney Tyrone Blue. Before Hartness had a chance to report his findings to your lawyer, he was picked up by the F.B.I. for jury tampering. I have already planned to visit him to find out how I can get your information from his computer. His wife has told me that after she gets his okay, she doesn't have a problem with this. "I will keep you informed as to my progress by letter."

After dropping this bomb on me, Ms. Conney stood up, smoothed out her dress and walked out of the visitation room.

I sat there astounded. One mention of Tyrone Blue's name and my brain began to accumulate piles of data, including my personal dislike of the man.

I was really stumped. The furthest thought from my mind was someone jury tampering. Why would an ex-cop turned, P.I. be involved in jury tampering? Better yet, why would a district attorney hire this man to investigate police corruption? Why not just call in internal affairs. I wanted more information.

The ordeal of this infamous dirty south had me longing for New York! I've heard inmates say "you can come here on vacation and leave on probation." Man! It's just not right!

A week later I received a detailed letter from Ms. Conney. It explained how the 58-year-old ex-cop turned P.I. crossed over a deadly line. Apparently, once he started to investigate the S.L.E.D. officers, he discovered that several officers had organized a gambling ring. This 'off the books' enterprise was worth millions.

Mr. Hartness had discovered all of the gambling house locations, the names of 7 officers involved, and how much money they each received. Somehow, maybe through a leak in the department, the officers found out about the growing case against them. Of course, they didn't want blemishes on their service records so they sent Mr. Hartness a briefcase filled with $100 bills with a note warning that if he didn't do as instructed, it could be fatal.

It really wasn't a hard decision to make once he opened the case. It held more money than he had ever imagined possessing in his lifetime. He didn't have any debt. Actually, he lived pretty comfortable but he had always dreamed of taking his wife on an extended vacation, somewhere exotic like Asia or Switzerland.

The note inside said that he was to bribe the jury into coming up with a favorable verdict against the evidence that he had helped to provide.

He should find the juror with the most debt and offer him or her $20,000 for helping swing the verdict against the evidence. He never thought it would backfire and he would be caught.

He thought he knew exactly how to manipulate the situation so that everyone would come out winners. The $20,000 payoff would not even be missed from his newfound wealth.

After finding his victim and making contact, they agreed on a location for payment. He delivered the money to the drop spot. Once he made it back to the comforts of his vehicle, he was swarmed by numerous F.B.I. agents.

Ms. Conney had permission from Mrs. Hartness to retrieve any information off her husband's computer she needed.

She ended the letter by telling me she would be visiting me soon.

I recited a quick prayer, thanking Jehovah for all his blessings.

I wanted to call my mother to tell her the good news because

I knew that it was her prayer that he listened to, not mine.

I decided to re-read the letter just to be sure I didn't miss anything.

Long-suffering and tolerance was the melody I was singing.

Chapter 26

Inseparable Nature

Denise and Judge Myers had their minds set to lunch, as was their customary rendezvous. Denise had been eagerly awaiting the next opportunity and lightly doused herself with Fuchsia, the fragrance that always caught the judge's attention. After a visit to an African health food store with another judge, Judge Myers had an extra surprise for Denise. He was told at the health food store by quite a vibrant looking 30-something year old female about the sexual benefits of eating Tiger Nuts. He had consumed them vigorously all morning long. He couldn't wait. Judge Myers was in excellent shape for a 66-year-old. He didn't drink or smoke and worked out whenever his schedule allowed. He was a complete ladies' man. He had also been happily married for over 30 years. He posed in the mirror wearing only his robe and a pair of socks.

Denise lightly tapped on the door, then walked inside. Judge Myers never turned around as she crept up on him and slid her arms around his waist. It was lunchtime!

Denise became unfaithful to her husband years earlier. And now it was time to block 'mister boring' from her mind completely so she could get her groove back. After it was over, she always felt dirty. She knew it was wrong, too, but she was in love with the old man.

It started off simple; a cup of coffee here and there, a little pat here, a little pat there. It was fun. She never believed it would go this far. She originally wanted to be his clerk full time, but once Mary got involved she took control.

Denise worked as Mary's head assistant covering up all her dirt and mistakes. Mary was always watching making sure everything was being handled properly. Her reputation was all she had. Nobody was going to mess that up. Nobody!

As the chamber doors closed behind her, he smiled and lit a cigar. He loved the sweet aroma after sex.

Denise rushed back to her desk to find stacks of files that weren't there before she left. Mary put them there. That was her way of letting Denise know she had been gone way too long.

It didn't bother her much because she'd get Susan to handle it anyway.

She sat there thinking about Judge Myers, how he made her feel, and wanting to run off with him forever.

Daydreaming was the best part of the whole thing. It made the situation that was happening seem less damaging. She wondered if he felt the same way after she'd left. But knowing him the way she did, it was far-fetched.

Another 30 minutes and it would be time for a 15 minute coffee break. She'd call the house to make sure the kids were home and give them their daily instructions. They would always ignore the ones she left on the fridge. Remembering to call is a daily routine. Married life had taken its toll. Watching the kids grow up and become adults was worth all the unfortunate disasters along the way.

"If it wasn't for the kids, I would've left long ago. Tim is too bossy and quick in bed. Not like the Judge, who was a professional at prolonging his ejaculations. Tim would finish and light up a cigarette before I'd get started. Foreplay was a foreign language. I guess it could be worse so why complain. At least he had a full-time job and spent time with the kids. He kept food on the table and ate most of it, but I guess that's what all men do. I never found phone numbers in his pockets or lipstick on his collar. Well, it's time to call the kids, I guess I'll finish separating the rest of these Pro se Motions later."

Denise looked over her shoulder to make sure nobody heard her thinking out loud. Everyone appeared busy handling clerical duties exactly as Mary liked it.

Chapter 27

Environmental Target

Prison life is rough. The simple way to sum it up is either you become a part of your environment or you can rise above it. I knew how to rub elbows with every kind of criminal from murderers to pickpockets.

I remember Richard Pryor said he use to tell jokes to keep inmates minds off his booty. I tell stories. It has the same effect. I also prayed a lot. I prayed and told stories whichever seem more feasible at the time.

I mostly prayed to Jehovah through his son Jesus once I found out his name. I also prayed for Ms. Conney to find out what happened to the other investigator, Mr. Hartness's, information that was supposed to help me get out.

My storytelling skills are up to par. I use them to talk my way into just about anything. I was also really good at talking my way out of things too. They tried to give me a nickname once of 'Lying Preach'.

Although a lot of inmates thought I was lying, my stories all held merit. Plus, I can fight. You didn't get to hang out with Mike Tyson the way I did unless you were solid.

Storytelling was my way to reminisce about the past and reminded me that there is hope for my future. It often amazes even me when I think of what I've been through and the people I've met and had dealings with.

I used to show pictures of my past like it was elementary show and tell day. My mementos convinced some, but most inmates were so nihilistic it didn't matter one way or the other.

I once told a story that happened during an All-Star Basketball event in Washington D.C. back in 2001. A host of friends and family and I, had booked rooms at the Hyatt Hotel downtown. There was a lot of paparazzi and groupies trying to get in the lobby area but security was tight. Without a room passkey, there was virtually no way to get inside.

My brother Big Fish, Zah, Jermaine Dupri, Florida Mike, cousin Tim and I were all standing around in the lobby getting tipsy before heading to the official All-Star Game after party where Snoop Dogg was performing.

About that time Big Shaq diesel got off the elevator and let me tell you that dude is a giant. He was sporting a full-length white mink coat with a matching 10 gallon white mink hat. This drew the attention of everyone in the lobby. Then right out the blue my dumb cousin Zah yelled out "Yo Shaq! You ain't no ballplayer, you a pimp!"

Everyone associated with the league and the ballers from the street burst into laughter. Shaq smiled but I could tell by his swag he wanted to put that huge alligator shoe across my cousin's throat for that outburst. Shaq walked over to where we were standing and shook all of our hands. His hand covered mine entirely.

Early Sunday morning after a night of partying my brother Fish and I were headed to the elevators to go to our hotel rooms. I noticed Grant Hill, his wife Tamia and their 3 or 4-year-old daughter were going to share the elevator with us.

The first thing that came to my mind was Tamia's hit song "Stranger in My House". I love that song. I looked down at their daughter. She reminded me so much of my own daughter that I reached out to pick her up. Surprisingly she reached back, which got the undivided attention of her parents. Tamia said to Grant, "Baby! Look at little mama. She's going to him."

Grant's eyes widened a little and he replied, "Maybe it's the jacket."

I was wearing a three-quarter length suede, rust-colored suede jacket. While holding their daughter for a brief moment, Tamia complimented me on my jacket. She asked me if she could feel the material. I could feel my brother smiling and my response was, "Sure!"

Mrs. Hill told her husband to feel how nice it felt. He rubbed his left hand over the sleeve and agreed. Our stop came, I put the little girl back down and Fish and I got off.

When we reached the room my brother said, "Man you are crazy! What made you do that?"

I responded, "Didn't their little girl look just like Brittney when she was that age?"

Big Fish then asked me about the sexy lady who slipped me her business card at the party. I almost forgot about that so I reached inside my jacket pocket to find it. I pulled it out and it read: Texanna, Head Assistant of Sean "Puffy" Combs.

One of the inmates yelled out, "Darn Unc! You were in the mix!"

I said, "Yeah. A little something like that."

        *   *

Ms. Conney had vanished into thin air. Her e-mail address and telephone number didn't exist anymore. I thought that my life was another episode of the Twilight Zone. I didn't know what to think at this point.

Could everyone who was supposed to help me be in coercion to keep me locked down? This can't be happening! My trial attorney, appellate attorney and 2 private investigators all conspiring against me. I have no other train of thought.

These were errors of monumental proportions.

Several very controversial issues needed to be addressed. I had to figure out a way to retrieve the information attained by the P.I.s', then I had to convey it to the courts.

My attorney had a legal obligation to get the P.I.s' info. Whatever she had found had to be vital in order for her to disappear like that.

A jailhouse lawyer named Wine heard about me and my troubles. He said he knew a reliable source and that he had contacted a P.I. that worked with inmates.

I didn't have many options and was willing to try anything at this point.

Wine was about 7 years older than me and had come in the system 12 years before I did. He was an old-school hustler with a murderous reputation. All the inmates, old and young, had much respect for him.

He was a great storyteller, too. But he only told his stories to people that he associated with. He told a lot of killing stories.

I always wondered why. He never denied anything that he did. If he did something, he'd say so! He also didn't lie at least not to me. I found him to be a stand-up kind of guy.

He told me how he got the nickname Wine. He said one day he went to school drunk. He was in middle school at age 12.

The principal called his father to come pick him up. He said that he was falling all over the desk and throwing up everywhere.

His head was spinning like a frisbee. He said he drank a bottle of Wild Irish Rose and some Old English 800.

He told me later after we became friends that his mother beat him all the way home.

After that, everyone called him Wine! Ironically, that was the first and last time he ever drank wine.

Chapter 28

True Love

As I walked through the steel visitation doors, my friend Anthony began rising from his chair. Always a fashionable fellow despite being close to 300 pounds, his clothes fit nicely and he looked great.

His beautiful wife Ann could have easily made millions flaunting her perfect body and fashionable style. She was a 10 plus.

In her usual gracious manner, she waited until Anthony and I finished exchanging daps and hugs before she stood up to greet me with a kiss on the cheek.

I enjoyed seeing those 2 together and it was evident that they made each other happy.

As soon as we were seated the handsome couple began bombarding me with flurries of complicated questions. Their copious energy told me I had to elaborate on each answer.

They wanted to know if I'd received the photographs of their nephew Jay's wedding.

Jay is Anthony's sister son, who went to college in Virginia. Years ago, Big Tone and I had visited Jay at school to make sure he was alright and handling his business.

I remembered Jay telling me he was in love. I told him if she's loyal and feels the same way about you, you should keep her. When I saw that look on his face, I knew he was serious. She had put it on him. It was funny watching someone else wear that 'hopelessly-in-love' look.

Nobody, not even Jay, knew that his college girlfriend was Oprah's niece. I expressed how happy I was for him. Looking at the photos of Jay's wedding and reception made me wish I could've been there.

It was no doubt a very extravagant occasion. It was held at Oprah's house in the Bahamas.

They said Oprah was dancing and acting like it was her wedding. She was mingling with the family like she'd known them all her life.

I kept smiling inside. I was happy. Jay is special in his own way. It was ironic that Jay's wedding occurred around the same time the South Carolina Court of Appeals reversed my trafficking by transportation charges.

Two years later and I still hadn't been given a court date to appear before a judge to have that case dismissed or to argue double jeopardy.

They had me sign release papers on June 28th, 2006. They even took me back to the county to be released.

The county decided to re-fingerprint me. They even recharged me with the same charges that the court had reversed.

When they called the prison and told them to come back and get me, everybody was shocked.

Tone and Ann always asked numerous questions each visit about me signing those release papers and why they never let me out. My answer would always be the same.

"I'm a 'political prisoner', kidnapped and held totally against my will."

I had filed numerous motions to the courts, trying to get out of this... lunatic asylum. None of them worked. I was out of my league and felt as if I was drowning.

The beginning of 2007, I thought strongly about filing a Federal writ, claiming The State violated my constitutional rights to a fair trial.

The writ was a Habeas Corpus petition. It is supposed to obtain immediate relief from illegal imprisonment. I should have been delivered from custody and brought before the courts. Its other purpose was to attack the constitutionality of the statute and proceedings in which the original conviction was obtained. Needless to say, that didn't happen.

I filed the habeas at the end of 2007. And now it's October 2009 and I haven't heard a thing.

Double jeopardy, insufficient evidence and abuse of the legal process were my main arguments.

I decided to change the subject because I was starting to get depressed and Ann looked like she had fallen asleep.

I asked Anthony if he still had a sleeping disorder. His eyes showed anger. Ann was now instantly awake. She had just ridden over 700 miles with him.

I hadn't thought about whether she knew or not… and he quickly answered "No! I went to therapy, got treated and now I'm cured."

The look he gave me let me know to quickly change the subject. Ann was trying to ask when he went to therapy. That's when I asked, "Was that a picture of Gayle at the wedding wearing the flowery dress?"

He said, "Yeah that was her!"

I smiled because I always thought Ms. King was a dime. She is breathtaking. I sat there thinking if I was out and at Jay's wedding, I would have had Gayle and Oprah all over the dance floor.

I told Anthony that I couldn't wait to meet Jay's wife, Oprah and Ms. King. It was just a matter of time before I'd have a chance to rub elbows with them.

I felt like by looking at the photos I already knew them.

A guard announced that visitation was complete.

I promised to send a copy of the photograph we'd taken.

Tone promised to keep me in the loop about life on the outside and to visit again soon.

I watched them get up and leave. It was a lonely feeling.

I sat there thinking about how smart Jay's wife was for not mentioning her relationship to Oprah until they graduated and he proposed to her. That was smart and respectable.

I also remembered Jay cutting up potatoes in the back of Anthony's restaurant at age ten.

He prepped the fish and shrimp while Big Tone and I ran around doing whatever we felt like.

Who would've thought that he'd grow up so fast and that the love of Jay's life would be Oprah's niece?

Chapter 29

Rule 60(b)

After 2 weeks of communicating with Mr. Lester Pearson, the P.I. my friend Wine suggested, he told me he didn't know how he could help me without an attorney.

He informed me about one of his associates/racquetball companions who was also an ex-United States Assistant Attorney General.

This same person, Mr. Carl Horn, also worked for a private law firm and recommend that I contact Mr. Horn at his law firm.

Mr. Pearson said he needed to know which direction to take to gather the evidence I needed to win my appeals.

I had my mother call the law offices of Adam, Cheney, Wallace and Associates in a 3-way conversation.

When the secretary answered, I asked to speak with Attorney Horn but was shocked to hear that he didn't work for the firm anymore. My mind was working faster than ever.

I told the secretary that I was an old friend in town on business and that I thought maybe Carl and I could get together so I could beat him in a game or 2 of racquetball before returning home.

I hoped to spark another kind of answer.

After a brief delay she said, "I can give you his cell phone number."

I thanked her, asked mom to dial the number and hoped that he would answer. The phone rang a few times before he answered, "Carl Horn here, how may I help you?"

I began by telling him my name. But before I could say anything more he wanted to know how I had his telephone number.

I decided that the truth was a good way to start whatever further relationship we might explore. I told him the entire story.

He was amazed. When I mentioned that Lester Pearson worked for me, that fact opened the door. Mr. Horn told me that he and Mr. Pearson were good friends and that he wanted to know what he could do for me.

I told him about signing release papers in 2006 and getting my conviction...overturned.

When I told him about getting re-fingerprinted and brought back to prison without ever going before a judge, he couldn't believe his ears.

He said he would research my case for a few weeks and to call him back.

After we hung up my mother said, "That was very nice of him to listen to your entire story. Maybe he can help you get out of prison."

That statement coming from her was sweet music to my ears.

Of course, I was anxious for the next few weeks to pass. I really couldn't wait to find Wine to thank him and update him on my conversation with the attorney.

The following day I received some not-so-good news.

It was Judge Myers' 29-page denial of my writ of habeas corpus.

As I read this document my head began to hurt.

His decision bent facts into a constructive fraud and it contained several inconsistent statements.

He was obviously pissed at me for filing a writ of mandamus.

It forced him to rule on my habeas corpus that had been sitting on his desk for over 2 years.

In no way could a federal judge constitutionally make such a ruling.

Maybe it was one of his law clerks. It said I had failed to show any evidence that I was entitled to relief on any of my claims.

He stated there were no genuine issues of material facts to be resolved. How could he ethically overlooked the 20 exhibits I had attached to my petition.

He granted summary judgment to The State and denied my petition. He had to be blind or disinterested not to see the flaws I pointed out.

I had documents showing everything from police department's fraudulent measures to get the indictments against me to an undeniable conflict of interest by my trial attorney Mr. Ericson, and proof of perjured verbal and written statements by The State witnesses.

Judge Myers' denial of my writ was a fundamental miscarriage of justice. A legal lynching.

I waited 21 days and had my mother 3-way Mr. Horn.

He sounded delighted to hear from me and immediately asked me what I was still doing in prison?

The only answer that made sense to me was "I don't know!"

He interrupted and added,

"How about I tell you that your whole case is nothing but a clerical mistake!"

I had to remember that my mom was still on the line so I refrained from cursing him. I wanted to hang up. I made an excuse to cut the conversation short and told him I'd call him again later. The phone went dead, which cut my mother off too.

I decided not to call her back. I needed some space to clear my head. I couldn't breathe, I felt played. What the heck did he mean by "My whole case is nothing but a clerical error?"

I needed Mr. Pittman's advice. He'd definitely know how to coach me in this situation state of affairs.

Chapter 30

Degree of Negligence

I had to pinpoint specifically what Mr. Horn meant by my case is… nothing but a clerical mistake. It had to be more than a clerical boo-boo. What was I missing? Should I have stayed on the line? Should I have been more particular when I spoke with him on the telephone? My mind was in a perfunctory, non-judgmental state. My thoughts were all over the place.

I could slowly feel myself losing to outrageous anger. I had to somehow pull it together.

I would usually be in bed by now but I knew I wouldn't be able to sleep until I reached some reasonable answer as to why this was happening to me.

To ease my mind I decided to re-read the denial of my habeas corpus petition by Judge Myers. His order had shot down all of my post-conviction remedies.

I saw again in my mind's eye the judge's signature. It had seemed simulated, almost counterfeit, for I had seen it on countless denial orders and oddly they were all perfectly identical as if someone had taken a picture. Can anyone consistently sign their name exactly the same way over months or in this case years? Had someone intervened and tampered with my exhibits? How come the judge never mentions anything about them? I needed to know why. Who had the power to expropriate my property? Maybe I would get to the bottom if I could find out the answer to any of my questions.

I thought about my trial attorney, Mr. Ericson. I thought about the police, the…I.R.S. I even thought about Judge Eve. Before going to bed I decided to draft a letter to the I.R.S. I knew that my charges carried a $250,000 fine owed to the I.R.S. I also knew that after my arrest, the police had seized all my personal property. In my draft, I decided to threaten to sue the agency for harassment and for violating The Fair Debt Collection Practices Act, among other things.

I knew my letter would have some kind of effect, but I had no idea how strong or useful it would be.

The judge's denial order did leave me some wiggle room to get back in court on an appeal. I just had to figure out how to incorporate any more evidence or information into my next brief. I had been lynched without due process and a fair trial, stripped of my liberties, my property and self-worth and ostracized from society as I knew it. I hoped for a microscopic chance that justice would peek from underneath her blindfold to stop what was happening to me!

It was back to the drawing board. I had to start from the beginning. Backtrack all my steps over. I decided to get on my knees and pray a long heartfelt prayer.

*   *

Everyone had something to drink in their hand at the annual Christmas party at City Hall where judges, lawyers, clerks, district attorneys and all of their family and friends gathered together for a common cause, money!

With conversation at its peak all around the room, envelopes filled with different amounts of cash were passed from hand to hand in the midst of handshakes, big hugs and smiles.

No monetary risks involved here. This money was all non-taxable profit called "General Donations."

Each envelope contained monetary awards. Judges and clerks seemed to receive most of the larger envelopes.

Many of these supposedly reputable, well-thought-of members of society who govern the land accept these envelopes.

In doing so they obstruct justice and the procedural process. Susan sat in the back of the large decorated room watching the grandiose behavior of her colleagues. It was a complete debacle, disillusioning of what Susan had thought to be her dream job.

She made a mental note to bring some sort of video recording device next year.

Judge Myers firmly massaged his wife's shoulders as he watched Denise dance slowly with her husband Tim. He wanted to cut in but soon thought better of such an act.

Mary stayed on point. She knew that her actions deserved and demanded payment in the form of one of those fat envelopes.

It was almost like a performance bond, a guaranteed procurement. It was secure.

Death row inmate Robert Bacon had drilled it in my head that clerks didn't have to discuss pro-se matters with anyone.

Most all pro-se petitions and briefs were denied automatically. That was Susan, Denise and Mary's job.

Litigation by licensed attorneys was another story altogether. Judges decided the outcome of motions sent in by lawyers.

With a new year approaching it was vital that the court records be as close to balanced as possible. It's the court's business! Robert said that balancing the court's records was what ran the country. It was a paper trail of the government against the citizens. A plague that infects every race, creed, tribe or social organization that is not part of their special clique circle. He said that anyone in the United States of America can become a defendant in a court of law. Impunity for those who snitch and become informants, for the beast.

It's part of the New World Order. Look at them!

Susan thought to herself to someone simply observing this party from the outside, they wouldn't suspect a thing.

Every move was camouflaged by those in the know.

Everyone there expected to receive cash for favors and knew how to keep their mouths shut.

In this particular court, this practice had been passed down traditionally from generation to generation.

Everyone involved closed their eyes to fraud, corruption and sin, but they readily opened their hands for an envelope.

Chapter 31

Seek and Find

The culmination of my life was drawing near. I believed everything had a start and finishing point.

As I opened the envelope from the clerk's office I could not stop smiling.

It was filled with all kind of documents. It was self-explanatory. The documents showed evidence that the petition that I filed to the court had been backdated an entire year. This meant a judge never saw the motion. He couldn't have.

A clerk had backdated my petition and exhibits so a judge could not rule in my favor on appeal.

This was not done inadvertently, it was intentional, premeditated!

I guess to find a clerical mistake, I had to start at the clerk's office. It made perfect sense to me now! I decided to call them, ask a few questions and tell them I needed a copy of all my previous filings. Yeah!

The clerk said, "Send us $14.10 for the 141 pages and you'll have it in a few days."

A few days later I received the package. I ripped it open. I was only interested in the first page of my exhibits and petition.

Both showed January 4th, 2009.

I clearly remembered filing the petition, exhibits and all the evidence supporting my claims on January 4th, 2010!

I couldn't believe they were bold enough to send me the evidence.

These dates proved clerical abuse of process.

Time was running out for filing my appeals and although I had filed the petition on time a judge never saw them.

To add to all that was happening, 3 officers approached claiming that I had back hole time, which meant that I had to go to segregation.

I laughed to myself cause everybody in the penitentiary knows if they owe back hole time. I knew for sure I didn't. None of the officers could explain why I had it. I was enraged and needed to calm down.

Being back in seg brought out these claustrophobic feeling I didn't like. It separated me from my legal papers and any outside help.

I mostly was concerned about my court papers. I had over 9,000 hours invested in studying legal matters. I considered myself almost an expert at filing briefs, petitions and responses from the opposing parties.

The next package from the court arrived and since I had already told my mom to only request the first page of my petition and of my exhibits, the clerk agreed to send them to me free of charge. It was the proof I needed.

As I read the documents I thought I'd need a medic. My entire body was shaking violently. One of the clerks had corrected the backdated documents at 9:54 p.m. The petition read "Filed: January 4, 2010, 9:54 p.m.

My exhibits hadn't been corrected. They still showed filed: January 4, 2009.

I put them both in another envelope with a letter to my mother requesting 10 copies of both documents. I would send the other papers once I got out of seg and reunited with my property.

I was now in possession of documented proof of use of a legal process in a manner not intended by law to achieve a purpose not contemplated by the law.

Mr. Harvey use to always say having information is as important as what you do with it!

I had already decided my first move. I also have plans to go beyond that by filing a petition to the United States Supreme Court.

I knew they only heard 2% of cases filed, but what the heck, you have to be in it to win and I had nothing to lose.

I wanted the courts, especially the darn clerks to know I knew what they was doing!

The pieces of this puzzle finally started to interlock and once again I started feeling hopeful about the outcome.

I had no real way to measure just how powerful these clerks were or how far their influence reached.

I truly believed something positive was in my future.

After some more investigating about even more damaging evidence: I learned there was a sign on the wall in the clerk's office that read: **"NEVER STAMP DOCUMENTS BEFORE 8 A.M. OR AFTER 5 P.M."**

Chapter 32

Intrinsic Value

I was asleep inside the segregation cell when the food tray door fell open. Officer Benge stood pigeon-toed on the other side holding a large manila envelope. When I got up to sign for it I saw bold red lettering that read: **CONFIDENTIAL I.R.S.**

I immediately thought about my draft letter and how I had stayed up writing it.

I sifted through the pages reviewing the variety of names, topics, titles and subjects. It was overwhelming! A brief letter stated that the documents I had requested were enclosed.

Of course, I couldn't find a signature or contact person's name anywhere inside the package. I knew this information was a godsend containing dirt on everybody involved in my case.

I had sent a 2-page letter threatening to sue the I.R.S.

In return they sent me enough evidence to sue everyone else. Unbelievable!

I finally found out what Gloria meant when she said that my paperwork was all messed up. What an understatement!

It turns out I hadn't needed the private investigator's information involving the judge and my ex-girl Sharon's friendship!

I now had the irrefutable, indisputable, unquestionable, overwhelming evidence I needed to burn all their corrupt behinds to smithereens!

The only thing I didn't have was an attorney. I knew I needed one. If not my efforts would be meaningless! I couldn't get past the crooked clerks.

I had plans on filing 4 civil suits, into the federal courts.

I figured that more evidence would surface during the discovery stages. With any luck, I might be able to get back in court and released on Rule 59, newly discovered evidence.

I had an idea to incorporate most of the evidence into my 7,191 words in my brief to the Supreme Court of the United States and send a copy to 1600 Pennsylvania Avenue to our President.

I thought it would help my case since President Barack Obama had just appointed Judge Wynn to sit on the circuit bench and he was the one that reversed my conviction on June 6, 2006.

I was sure that when I filed my petition for a hearing en banc and all the judges were in the same room to vote whether or not to hear the case, he would see his name and vote in my favor.

I was going for the gusto. I would contact World News, 60 Minutes, 20/20, USA Today and any other media source that would listen. I even thought about writing a screenplay. I'd call it "Rule 60(b)".

That's what Mr. Horn said went wrong with my case.

For 3 months I diligently searched for an attorney to take my case and could not find one lawyer who was willing.

I contacted attorneys in North and South Carolina, New York, Florida, Tennessee, Virginia, Ohio, even California. When I couldn't find one in Atlanta I began to lose hope again.

Then one day I was watching Oprah's last talk show before she started OWN.

It was as if she was speaking directly to me. She said, "Do it yourself! Nobody is going to take pride in your work like you will."

At that moment it was like being struck by lightning. I decided to file the lawsuits myself.

The first lawsuit was against the S.B.I. agent, Tyrone Spann.

He had lied through his teeth. Global positioning on his cell phone placed him 40 miles away from the scene at the time of my arrest. He said he was right there when it happened.

He testified at my trial saying he arrived in time to see me and Jack exit Sharon's Cadillac at 6:15 p.m.

He also said, "I was in the interview room with Juwan while Officer Buster and Agent Black questioned him."

His perjury is what made them convict me. It connected me to the vehicle and showed domination and control.

I'll wait to see what happens with his lawsuit and then I'll sue Mr. Ericson!

Chapter 33

Constitutional Chaos

The U.S. Marshall served my complaint on Agent Spann. He signed for it and aggressively tore it open. When he realized who was suing him he almost had a heart attack.

There in his hands was a 10-page complaint containing 60 paragraphs of statements he had to agree with or deny.

I'd had the document typed professionally. I found the company while reading the prison legal news magazine.

Spann thought about his career and his family. He thought about all the messy trials that would not have had convictions without his help.

He knew he needed legal advice with only 20 days to find it.

He thought about the consequences and the damage it would cause once the truth came out. He knew there would be numerous cases that would require review and all would result in lawsuits. He held the paper tight. He wanted to tell his wife, but he decided to wait before pushing the panic button.

My plan was to file another lawsuit every 30 days, enough time to write it out, get it typed and filed.

I knew that none of the defendants in my lawsuits would be able to answer my complaints without an attorney.

I was proud of myself for being able to write a legal document and then write a response within days.

I had learned from the best, Mr. Pittman and my attorney friend in New York. Always argue what you can prove.

I knew that the opposing attorneys would go crazy trying to figure out if I could prove any of my allegations.

I had exclusive control.

The fabricated evidence against me was about to be heard, analyzed and determined. The wrongdoers were gonna go down.

Spann was now the target of my attack, was now a defendant in the U.S. district court accused of perjury, obstruction of justice and being involved in a profiteering, oppression and scam.

His neglect of duty and failure to perform his moral obligations was malicious, mental cruelty, not to mention outright dishonest and illegal.

I'm surprised I made it through this time without medication.

Lucrative or not, it was just plain wrong and unreasonable!

I wondered how they all slept at night.

I made sure there were few loopholes in my complaint, which involved joint offenses linking 3 different agencies.

Since my trial attorney didn't act under the auspices of federal law according to the court's ruling, I decided to file each suit separately with a long list of invasion of principle and property violations. I couldn't wait for my day in court.

The tables would be turned!

Gloria's Prediction

I sent my trial attorney's suit to the Federal Court on October 17, 2011.

By November 21, 2011, the Federal Court rendered a decision saying "The plaintiff in the case Juwan Jackson, has a legal malpractice claim against his Trial Attorney, John Ericson, for failure to attend the I.R.S. Hearing or notifying his client of the hearing.

On December 5, 2011, I filed suit against A.T.F. Agent, Carl Black. On January 30, 2012, I filed a complaint on 6 Columbia, South Carolina police officers. Altogether the suits involved 13 defendants, including the agencies that they belonged to.

I was demanding a cool $2,044,000 each.

Twenty-six million dollars could not make up for all the time and damage it caused but it was a start.

Gloria had predicted it all. She must have had insight from Satan himself.

I had started studying the Bible with Jehovah's Witnesses and started to learn what the Bible really taught.

By December 26, 2014, I am sitting in a segregation cell thinking about my daughter and what's taking her so long to respond to my letter dated November 7th. I knew Barkima always dragged when it came down to doing things she needed to do. She had always been that way. I love her and continue to wait.

Susan never did end up going against her colleagues, although she did speak her mind and knew in her heart that there was flagrant wrongdoing in that office. She was fired in April, by Mary.

I am still in litigation with Federal and State attorneys over the $26 million, but the judge won't appoint counsel.

This is far from a reasonable world that we live in and according to the Bible and Jehovah's promise, I won't have to put up with this system much longer.

I have 4 years, 4 months and 8 days left to do pursuant to my judgment and commitment papers.

That's a drop in the bucket compared to the 36 years I started with.

Filing lawsuits had become addictive. I am starting to draft a complaint against the State clerks.

I wish I could be a fly on the wall when they get served!

The End

About The Author

Anthony Williams, the author of many lustrous stories, was born in Brooklyn, New York. He lives in North Carolina with his family. He is the CEO of Prisoners Potential Publishing Plus.

To learn more visit: www.pppplus4inmates.org

Send order form with money order or certified check to:

PPPPlus

P.O. Box 242790

Charlotte, NC 28224

www.pppplus4inmates.org

Ship To:

Name_____

Address _____

City, State, Zip _____

Email (optional) _____

Product	Price	Quantity	Subtotal
Clerical Mistake	19.95		
Shipping (per book)			
Total (USD only)			

Made in the USA
Middletown, DE
04 August 2020

14204900R00136